save the teens:

preventing suicide, depression and addiction

by Carolyn C. Zahnow

with contributions by Katharine Leslie, PhD

by Carolyn C. Zahnow

with contributions by Katharine Leslie, PhD

The information presented in this book is based on research and experience. To address gender issues in writing, I chose to randomly alternate male and female pronouns.

All illustrations are the original artwork of J. Cameron Stephenson and are the property of Carolyn Zahnow.

To purchase copies of this book, send your name, address, and a check for $20.90 (includes $3.95 shipping and handling) to Carolyn Zahnow, 105 River Watch Lane, Youngsville, NC 27596. For special orders contact (919) 368-6286 or www.save-the-teens.com.

First Edition
Cover photos by Jaclyn Whitted and Cameron Stephenson
Cover design by Cynthia Meyer

Published by Brand New Day Publishing
Printed by Fidlar Doubleday

Zahnow, Carolyn: save the teens: preventing suicide, depression, and addiction
– 1st edition.

Acknowledgments

"save the teens" has been a labor of love for many people in my life. I have received so much encouragement for its completion and success that it makes my heart proud. And if I forgot anyone, you know how I am so just know that I thank you, too. So let me start the hands clapping for the following VIPs in my life:

My ever faithful, endearing, and understanding (most of the time) husband, Dan. My sister, Kristie Rhodes, who has provided her design expertise on many occasions, but mostly for her empathy of losing her nephew and my son, Cameron. Katharine Leslie, Ph.D., for her wisdom of editing and knowledge of mental illness and adolescents. Meredith Hailey, my wonderful therapist – you have helped me weather this storm by providing a searchlight of hope in all my undertakings. Bebee Bason and the Foundation of Hope for their continued support for my mission to help teens in North Carolina. Liza Weidle for so much! Thanks, Liza, for your leadership. Elaine Klonike for her opinions, for being a reader, and providing edits. Also the members of TAF (Triangle Area Freelancers). I have met so many "Taffies" who have helped me along the journey of nonfiction writing. Julie Contakos for providing a concise index, which I insisted on. Megan Cutter (and Barton) for always being there when I have a writing question and providing journaling tips. Mary Storms who took the first crack at editing the book with lots of helpful suggestions. Alice Osborn, my "feelings" editor. Thanks for your continued support. Cynthia Meyer for providing graphic design for the beautiful cover and her ongoing friendship. Mary Martin – you are my hero! Kristie Plaga, thanks for being there for each and every disaster during my life.

Anna Warren for being a young adult reader – hang in there, Anna! Dr. Martha Giles in Flower Mound for being a reader, writing my first review, and providing encouragement. Wake Forest Survivors of Suicide support group – you all help me more than you know! Elizabeth Johnson, I feel we are kindred spirits and I value your co-facilitating more than you know. Touched by Suicide support group in Flower Mound, TX – Sue Endsley – you rock! Lori Herbst, "Magistra" Mel Santos, and Denise Harmon, from Marcus High School and Dale Jackson Career Center for the love and guidance they provided Cameron, and then me after his death. Jaclyn Whitted, photographer extraordinaire – thanks for the cover photo "smashup." Dr. Uros Zrnic, M.D., for his time in helping me to understand Cameron's illness. His input on the mental illness section helped tremendously. Dr. Drew Bridges, M.D., for believing in me and my suicide prevention causes. My family's support in all my efforts in suicide prevention – hugs and kisses.

To Cameron's many Texas friends – thanks for putting up with the "mother hen" I was for so long. I am confident that you all will make wise decisions in your lives and be strong along the way. Thanks for taking care of me. (Lauren, Kelly, Braxton, Everett, Amber, Jaclyn, etc.) And finally, our sweet little dog, Sheila, for providing me the comfort I needed after losing my ray of sunshine.

Dedicated to

Jace "Cameron" Stephenson

May 29, 1987 - August 11, 2005

This book is a chance for us to share your wisdom with the world since
you were unable to do so. We miss you and will keep your
memory close to our hearts forever.

Until we meet again.

To the Reader

You will find "save the teens" is set up differently from other books you've read. With the exception of the Introduction and the first chapter, "Cameron's Final Day," the right pages contain information and statistics and the left pages contain personal stories by the author and her deceased son, Cameron Stephenson, as well as his artwork.

You can read this book several different ways. You can read the right side all the way through and then go back and read the left side, or vice versa. Or read the left side in conjunction with the right side as they often correspond.

The text on the front cover is an actual blog written by Cameron during his last summer – may he rest in peace now.

Table of Contents

Introduction

August 11, 2005, 7:05 a.m. At home in bed. "Why is Cameron's phone ringing and ringing? I've told those girls not to call here and let the phone ring off the hook! OK – I'm getting up to answer his phone and cuss someone out!" I walk up the stairs to answer my 18-year-old son's ringing phone. I see the attic stairs are down. I'm wondering why. I move closer. I see Cameron's feet dangling in the attic opening. I remember screaming: *"Cameron, please don't go. Come back to me! I'll do anything you want. God, no, no, no. Please don't leave me. Come back. Baby, life's not that bad. Come back to me!"*

~~~~~~~~~~~

My heart pounds, almost out of my chest, as I write this and read it over and over. This moment, and the ones of me trying to bring my son back to the world of the living are etched in my memory forever. Losing a child to suicide is the worst imaginable pain anyone can live through. If you want to call it living.

I wrote this book in the hope of preventing other teens from taking their lives. They are so worthy of life, yet they are usually too depressed to realize this. I know it is imperative to alert teachers, parents, friends – whoever teens associate with – about the signs and symptoms of depression and suicidal risks. But that's not enough. I also want to encourage anyone who is concerned about a teen to share these concerns with others who can help, as well as with the teen's parents -- even if the parents are in denial.

> *If you're currently in crisis or know someone who is, call 1-800-273-talk*

Parents often need confirmation from others before taking action. And once parents know their child is at risk, they need to know what action to take. After my son's death, I spoke to many audiences regarding suicide and depression and was surprised to hear over and over again, "But what do we do? Who do we call?" So I wrote this book to be sure that suspecting parents know where to turn for help.

Recently I started rereading a book on teen depression that I had begun during the trials and tribulations of life with Cameron. When I discovered different pen marks in the book, my heart flooded with emotion. The notations were made by Cameron; he had also started reading the book. And it appeared that he hadn't finished the book either. Why not? Maybe we didn't want to take the time or didn't think it applied to our situation. In any case, I urge you to read the chapters in this book that you need now in order to save a teen from depression or possibly suicide. You don't have to read the whole book, you can go straight to the Help section.

The book begins with my last heart-breaking day with Cameron and goes on to describe the aftermath. It's a story that needs to be told. It's jarring and distressful. I then describe many troubling aspects of my son's life with honesty and reflection so that you can recognize similar signs in a teen or young adult you hold dear. And because suicide is highly correlated with depression and addictions, I include research on depression, addictions (particularly methamphetamine), and suicide and suicide survivors; Cameron suffered from depression and addiction since shortly after his dad died when he was 15 years old. Three years later, he was dead.

Cameron's poetry, journal entries, and illustrations displayed within this book were found after his death and are quite telling of his state of mind. If they had been discovered prior, I would have taken steps to institutionalize him. Although I don't torture myself thinking that this intervention would have saved his life, who can know for sure?

Perhaps reading this book will be your call to arms, and you will become a gatekeeper in helping our teenagers who cannot help themselves.

Carolyn Zahnow
(Cameron's mom)

Only one spore to bleed its wing.

Every understanding bellows with necessary uniquity.

Violent foreigner on the fence post.

Seventy-two spectacular suicides.

All leftiness elaborating her discomfort.

Torture always emitted sweet sweet.

Her burgundy wardrobe stained with all.

Fourteen eternities unfold for bearing arms.

Team reaming with willful shadows.

Sealing never slept her sweet.

Soft pillows of friendly needles

One more bundle to load

Can't the coronary consciousness precede faith?

Cariosity under burning bridges.

Feeble fury sweeping national toys.

Parting though culinary sapphires.

ONE

Cameron's Final Day

*This chapter was my first journal entry after Cameron's death. It was
written two weeks later and illustrates how raw my emotions were at the
time. As painful as it was, I felt I had to put these memories on paper.
Little did I know, it would be the beginning of a whirlwind of research and
journal writing for the next year. I often think writing, reading, and talking
about my son's suicide was how I survived his death without going crazy.*

August 11, 2005 – Thursday, the day of my son's death. My good friend
Bonnie was visiting from Florida and was due to return home early that
morning. My husband Dan was out of town all week on a house-hunting
trip to Raleigh (where we were planning to re-locate) and was due to
return that afternoon. Bonnie was up at 4:00 a.m. that Thursday morning
getting ready for her flight. I got up at 4:45 so we'd have time for tea
before I drove her to the airport. We were in the kitchen chatting waiting
for the tea to finish brewing when Cameron showed up at the back door.
He scared me because he was dressed in a black T-shirt and it was still
dark outside and I couldn't quite make out his form. Plus, I was not
expecting him to come home at 5 a.m. because the light I had left on for
him in the foyer was turned off. I naturally assumed he was in bed where
he should have been. But obviously he had been home earlier and turned
off the light before heading out again. He came in the house with a large
sketchpad. He almost always had a sketchpad in his hands. I didn't see
what was on it. He was damp from the early morning rain. I fussed at him

about being up all night and told him he needed to get some sleep because he had to go to work at his new job at Wolfe Camera later that morning. He said he didn't have to be there until 10:30 a.m. so he had plenty of time. I asked where he had been and he said he'd been skateboarding and then went by his girlfriend Lauren's house. This was not his plan when I had spoken to him on the phone earlier in the evening; he had told me he was going to give his friend Nicki a ride home from work and would be home at 12:30 p.m.

As Cameron was heading upstairs, I told him that Dan was coming back today. Cameron responded disappointedly, "Already?" I wasn't sure if his tone was due to the reminder of our impending move to North Carolina or because he and his stepdad, had not been the best of buddies lately. This is understandable as Cameron had started using meth a couple of years prior and was making home life very stressful.

Cameron headed upstairs for bed – I thought. Bonnie and I left for the airport around 5:30 a.m. I dropped her off and headed back home. I probably arrived home by 6:15 a.m. but I really don't know what time it was – could have been earlier or later. The house was quiet. I did not go up and check on Cameron; I only did that if it was noon and he was still in bed. I decided to lie down on my bed and close my eyes. I didn't change my clothes or get under the covers. I just wanted to enjoy the quietness and coolness of the early morning. I dozed off but was awoken at 7:05 a.m. by Cameron's landline ringing in his room. After four rings it switched over to the fax machine in the loft. The loft was located at the top of the spiral staircase in our house and overlooked the family and dining room areas as well as the foyer. This was where I read emails, stayed in touch with long distance friends, created greeting cards, and had many conversations with Cameron. Because of the openness of the loft to the rest of the house, the phone ringing was pretty intrusive.

I ignored the ringing as long as I could, thinking it must be one of Cameron's girlfriends. It finally stopped, but after five minutes it rang again and then again ten minutes later. I was puzzled as to why Cameron had not picked up the phone and then I became furious that whoever it was would not stop calling. I jumped out of bed ready to grab the phone and tell someone off. I went up the stairs heading for the loft. On the other side of the loft was a hallway, which led to a bedroom used as a craft room, Cameron's room, his bathroom, a game room and the attic. Upon reaching the landing of the loft, I saw the attic stairs were down. I thought, "That's strange." Walking across the loft and getting to the other side of the attic stairs, I saw why. My Cameron was hanging above the stairs with a rope around his neck. He had tied the rope to a rafter in the attic in close proximity to the opening. I rushed up the shaky stairs, wrapped my arms around his chest, and pulled up trying to relieve some pressure off his neck. I was screaming at him, "Cameron! Don't leave me. I'll do anything."

No response. His color was not good; there was saliva coming from his mouth and snot from his nose.

I thought, "'I've got to cut him down." I mentally located where a knife might be but knew the kitchen was too far away. Scissors! There were some in the craft room just beyond the stairs. I found the orange-handled scissors and quickly ran back up the attic stairs and cut the damn rope.

Cameron fell to the floor, and then I was scared that if he was still alive the fall might have killed him. He fell and lay partially in his bathroom and partially in the hallway. He was limp.

I knew I must call 911. I called and blurted out all the information the dispatcher needed. He told me to perform CPR on Cameron. I had to get Cameron flat, which was not easy because he was six feet tall and lay crumpled in the hallway. I don't know how but I managed somehow to stretch him flat and started doing what the dispatcher told me.

I had to first check his mouth and see if there was anything in it. His tongue was already rigid. I knew there was no hope for my baby boy. But I had to try to bring him back to me, so I followed the dispatcher's instructions, "Hold his nose and breathe into his mouth two times so you can see his chest rise." At first this didn't work but with the second attempt I could see his chest rise and my hope rose with it. I pressed on his chest 10 times and repeated the mouth-to-mouth procedure.

I do not remember how long I did this, but stopped when I heard banging on the door – EMS had arrived as well as a couple of police officers. I ran down the stairs to open the front door. Oddly, I first secured our dog, Sheila, in the guest room downstairs so she would not run out the door; maybe I realized she was my only surviving baby. I don't remember what I said to the EMS guys when I opened the door, I only remember leading them upstairs to where Cameron lay.

One of the police officers led me downstairs while they worked on Cameron in the loft. While they tried to save him, I felt in my heart he was gone. I don't know how long I waited before going back upstairs and pleading with the EMS guys, saying, "If there is no hope of saving Cameron, please do not take him to the emergency room." Cameron went to the ER a couple years back after having a seizure at a friend's house and he hated being there. A neurologist was never able to really pinpoint what caused his seizure. Cameron finally confessed that he had been abusing Triple C (a cough and cold medication). It was likely that the combination of Triple C, staying up all night, and the strobe light effect on a video game he had played at his friend's sleepover sparked the seizure. The EMS team responded with "We're doing the best we can." Turns out Cameron had to go to the ER after all so a doctor could pronounce him dead.

I left the EMS team working on Cameron and returned downstairs where Lauren, one of Cameron's two girlfriends, was sitting in the dining room. I overheard her telling a detective, "He told me to call him back in an hour." Thinking Lauren was the last to speak to Cameron and possibly being the reason that Cameron made his fatal decision, I could not face her. Instead, I went to my bedroom to prepare for a trip to the hospital. I didn't find out until later that day it was Kelly, Cameron's other girlfriend, who heard his last words at 6:11 a.m. According to Kelly, Cameron called her from his cell phone and told her he loved her and would pick her up from work later that day. Little did she know Cameron was in the attic at the time preparing the rope that would end his life.

While in my bedroom, I called Dan before he left Raleigh for his flight home. I told him about finding Cameron and asked him to get home ASAP. I still did not know for sure if Cameron was dead or alive. I must have felt there was a chance for Cameron because I put a pair of jeans and a light sweater in a bag to take to the hospital. I thought it might be cold in the hospital and wanted to be prepared in case I would be spending a lot of time there. I heard the EMS team coming down the stairs. They carried Cameron on a stretcher with a ventilator. Lauren and I watched helplessly as they loaded him into the ambulance. A police officer asked if I wanted to ride with Cameron in the ambulance. I said, "No." I don't remember why I made that choice. I must have thought I was going to drive myself to the hospital.

A police officer told me that I could not drive because I was in shock. He volunteered to drive me and asked if there was anyone I could call to be with me at the hospital. Before leaving, I went into Cameron's room and picked up his green writing book with flocked designs on the cover thinking I'd have time to read it while waiting for Cameron's release from the hospital. I think the officer was right, I was in shock.

I called my mother first and she had a hard time understanding what I was saying. I'm sure I was babbling something about Cameron yet I don't remember what it was. She thought I was my sister Angela. She says Angela and I sound alike when we are distressed. I called Mary Jane next. I thought of calling Micki but she was too far away and had a new baby. Then I thought of Linda but she wasn't a close enough friend. Mary Jane was a nurse and we'd had some good talks in the past. Fortunately when I called her, she was home and ready to help me. She arrived at the hospital shortly after I got there. She met me in an isolated room reserved for relatives of dying patients. The police officer who drove me to the hospital was there and a retired minister joined us. No one knew what to say, I didn't know what to say. I was extremely uncomfortable. I felt caged.

Finally the ER doctor came in and told me Cameron was dead. I let the tears flow then, I was in agony. I could not save my baby and now he was gone. The doctor said they did everything they could, and I knew in my heart it was hopeless. The reserved room was full of people at that point and I only knew one, Mary Jane. Thank God for this angel. She helped me so much. There are so many questions to be answered and decisions to be made when our loved ones are dead or dying. Questions a parent should never have to answer. "Where do you want Cameron's body to be sent?" "Was Cameron an organ donor?" He and I never talked about this and I wasn't sure, so I said, "No." This was a decision I later regretted. There were insurance and hospital forms to fill out and signatures needed everywhere. Mary Jane was there to help me through it all.

Soon all I could think about was getting out of the sterile hospital and into the comfort and safety of my own home. But we had to wait for the medical examiner to arrive to sign the death certificate. He was driving over from Fort Worth, which felt like an eternity. The medical examiner helped me make some very difficult decisions regarding what to do with Cameron. Do I ship him back to North Carolina to be buried beside his father? Do I bury him in Texas? The medical examiner mentioned cremation. I thought this was the perfect solution so I could keep Cameron with me always. He asked if I wanted to see Cameron before we left. At first I said no, but then I started having some regrets about that decision and changed my mind. I thanked him.

So on the way out of the Lewisville Medical Center, I said goodbye to my Cameron. He looked more peaceful than when I found him. He was rigid, so I didn't want to do much touching. However, I did run my fingers through his hair and to my surprise it was quite clean. Probably from being out in the rain or maybe he had taken a shower that night. I told him he was my friend. I probably told him I loved him but I don't remember. I only remember saying he was my friend. And that's true. We went through a lot together for eighteen years. I wanted the world for him but when his dad died, it seemed Cameron's world came to an end – hopefully he was now in a place free of worry and too many decisions.

We left the hospital by 10:00 a.m., a little over two hours since we'd arrived. They pronounced Cameron dead at 8:08 a.m. on August 11, 2005. But I felt in my heart he was gone by 6:15 a.m. My mother called my cell phone while Mary Jane drove me back to the house. All three of my sisters were at her house. I spoke to each one. They were in tears. I ached to be with my family in Raleigh.

Before leaving the hospital, the investigator gave Mary Jane a report to complete, which we did after arriving home. We sat in the breakfast nook at the table – I re-told the story of finding Cameron while Mary Jane wrote it all down. She thought of things that I had forgotten, such as did I put the attic stairs back up after cutting him down? I think I must have or else I could not have gotten to Cameron very easily after he fell to the floor. She helped me think about which funeral home to select. At home in Raleigh I knew these kinds of things, but not here in Texas. I chose a local funeral home close to our home and to Cameron's friends. Mary Jane also gave me ideas for the service and who I needed to call. The funeral home required a signed release for Cameron to be autopsied – a law in Texas if death was not by natural causes. The funeral director offered to come over so I could sign it. That was truly nice of him. He didn't offer much guidance, but he probably knew I wouldn't comprehend much at that time.

Dan called me around 1:00 p.m., and Mary Jane took me to the airport to pick him up. Unfortunately, I had failed to tell Dan that Cameron was gone. I just assumed he knew this from my earlier frantic call, but all he knew was that Cameron had gone to the hospital. I think he asked me about Cameron on the ride home. But I don't remember telling him everything until we were sitting at the kitchen table. Then I told the story as if I were a child. Slow, broken sentences.

Mary Jane left shortly after the telling of the story. Dan was here to take care of me now, and all the upcoming details. While Dan was outside saying good-bye and thank you to Mary Jane, I curled up on the couch and cried so hard saying "No, no, no!" and clutching my wrist so tightly that I had bruises the next day. My natural coloring hid the dark bruising so most people didn't notice. But I could see the bruising and I knew it signified the deep hurt of losing Cameron. Sometimes, even after four years, I find myself clutching my arm too hard.

A self-portrait entitled

"Take That"

AFTERMATH: TELLING THE WORLD

Constant telephone rings filled the remainder of the day. Lauren's parents, Kelly's aunt, my relatives, friends, so many people. Word spread like wildfire. The towns of Flower Mound, Raleigh, Bear Grass, and Washington, North Carolina, were crying for Cameron.

I left phone messages for Cameron's stepmom and his half-sister, who lived in North Carolina (Cameron's dad re-married shortly after our divorce, and they had a daughter, making Cameron a big brother). Finally she left me a quick voice message, which revealed she didn't understand the gravity of the situation. I left more terse voice messages and she called back the next day. When I spoke to her and the news sunk in, she screamed in agony.

I knew I still had to let my colleagues at Nokia know about Cameron, so I called a co-worker. She told everyone else. I heard from people in Irving as well as in the New York office – it was very touching. Sometime that day I left a message for Cameron's psychiatrist. He called me back and was so saddened by the news.

The following days were a blur for me as I suffered from posttraumatic stress. I was unable to sleep, so my doctor prescribed a sleep medication for me. This, along with the sound of the TV, would finally help me rest. Yet every morning I would awaken at 6:15 a.m. - the time I determined Cameron had taken his last breath.

Two weeks after the memorial services in both Flower Mound and back home in Raleigh, life was extremely hard. Just walking our dog down the street was difficult. I felt I would collapse. My sister, Kristie, recommended I start journaling, especially since I loved to write. I started the next day and captured my thoughts on paper every morning for an entire year. I was able to put some of the questions that constantly bombarded me on paper. It freed up my mind tremendously. At the same time, I started doing research on suicide, teen depression, and methamphetamine; my son had suffered years of depression and had been addicted to methamphetamine.

Through my research I discovered support groups for people who had lost someone to suicide. And there was one just up the street from our house that met twice a month. I started attending these meetings and found so much comfort because the people there had all lost someone close. We could talk about suicide, the pain incurred by it, and how it's so different from any other death.

I attended meetings for a month and learned of a grief support group, which I needed badly. I had to put aside the overwhelming questioning of why my son killed himself and confront the grief of his death.

Dan and I attended all six sessions. We went into the sessions in a fog and came out better prepared to face the future without our son. I still needed to fill my days and my head with something other than the death of my only child. I began substitute teaching and working part time at a retail craft store. I occupied my mind with work. The teaching was great and I loved being around the kids. I preferred substitute teaching at middle schools; I hoped I could help a teen or two by being a friend and a good listener. After several months, I gained enough courage to sub for one of Cameron's former high school teachers. All of the kids in that class knew Cameron, but he and I had different last names so they didn't recognize me as his mother. I think that was for the best. If they had known, they may have felt sad and unable to do their work. I knew I had climbed a mountain when I agreed to walk back into his high school. It was good to see some of his teachers I had become close with when Cameron was there. We worked hard to get him through to graduation. We succeeded, but sometimes I think, what difference did it make?

I'm still grateful for the memory. I feel pride in my heart when I think of my son walking across the stage to receive his high school diploma. His death cannot take that away from me – nor all the other moments of our life together.

I am...

I am a worthless pawn of society.
I wonder what the meaning of life is.
I hear the whispers of memories lost.
I see only what the world lets me see.
I want to be in love.
I am a worthless pawn of society.

I pretend to be cheerful for the ease of others.
I feel a twist in my heart for memories that will never be.
I touch the smooth, cool air of yet another day.
I worry about feelings of others.
I cry for the loss of a best friend.
I am a worthless pawn of society.

I understand that the one thing certain about my future is that I won't be anymore.
I say that people should do what they think is right no matter what gets in their way.
I dream to get back what was taken away from me.
I try to keep my own opinions to myself.
I hope to go over the speed bump as quickly as possible.
I am a worthless pawn of society.

Cameron Stephenson

TWO

Depression

Before we can discuss teen depression specifically, it is helpful to understand depression in general. You've likely heard a lot about depression these days, albeit mostly from sales-seeking drug manufacturers and their mass advertising campaigns. But the good that has come from this plethora of ads is that depression is no longer a forbidden subject. These ads have served to educate the public and persuade many individuals to seek help when they might not have done so otherwise. People are more aware that depression is a disease just like cancer or sclerosis of the liver. What most people don't know, however, is that there are different types of depression.

Some people experience a general sense of malaise called Dysthymia, which is milder than major depression and doesn't seem to be related to specific events or life conditions. Others, like me, experience event-related depression, meaning it's associated with a normal life crisis and bereavement. The depression and anxiety I felt after losing my son lasted for the better part of a year. It was considered a major depressive episode. The Diagnostic and Statistical Manual of Mental Disorders (DSM-IV) published by the American Psychiatric Association, defines a major episode as a period of two weeks or longer of a depressed mood or loss of interest or pleasure along with at least four other symptoms of change. Specifically:

CAMERON'S *changing* **history**

Cameron was only three months old when his dad left us – not my choice – and two years old when we divorced. Dan and I met when Cameron was 5 while he and I were living in Raleigh. A year later, Cameron went to live with his dad in Washington, N.C. so that I could return to college. When Cameron was 10 years old, Dan and I married and Cameron came to live with us a year after that. Just one year later Dan's job required that we move to Texas. Three years later Cameron's dad died, and three years after that Cameron ended his life. Now that I look back, I think these were a lot of changes for a child to endure.

Cameron always wanted his dad and me to get back together. He spent alternating weekends between his dad's home and mine when we lived in the same state, until his dad died when Cameron was 15. Cameron loved his dad. It's likely that situational events of the divorce and the death of his dad contributed to Cameron's depression and substance abuse.

Dan and I moved back to Raleigh one year after Cameron's death as we had no longer had a reason to remain in Texas, nor could I continue to live in the house where my son died.

- Significant weight loss
- Insomnia or hyperinsomnia
- Fatigue or loss of energy
- Feelings of worthlessness
- Diminished ability to think or concentrate
- Recurrent thoughts of death

In my case, I was fatigued and felt like I was just going through the motions of living. I thought I would never smile again or feel any joy in my life. I feared I would continue to wake up every morning at 6:15, the time Cameron took his last breath. But in time, and with the help of family, friends, and great therapists, I once again experienced joy upon seeing daffodils bloom in March, and fortunately was able to sleep the majority of the time. I felt at times (and still do sometimes) like I was living in my own private hell as a result of losing my only child. I still miss my son like crazy, but I tell myself at least he is free from the demons of his own mind.

Unlike my depression, Cameron's was a chronic condition. Cameron likely suffered recurring mild depressive periods throughout his life. The death of his father compounded this condition. As a result, he experienced a major depression that lasted for years. He must have felt miserable and terrified, so much so that he self-medicated with drugs and alcohol in an effort to squelch his agony. It all turned on him one day, when he finally determined ending his life was the answer to ending his pain and misery.

Stealing days never seemed so easy.

Forever summer insists on growing...

The days I always longed for now seem to be showing

that prison wasn't so bad.

Naturally, not all people who experience depression take such a drastic measure. Unfortunately, though, depression is all too prevalent in today's teenagers, which places these teens at high risk for suicide. In 2008, RTI International reported that 2.1 million young people aged 12 to 17 experienced a major depressive episode during 2007. What a phenomenal number! Sometimes parents attribute their teen's irritability to hormones or simple teen rebelliousness. However, persistent unhappiness or moodiness is not normal – for anyone.

A depressive disorder is a disease that affects mood, thoughts and behavior; it is a biochemical brain dysfunction. Here's how it happens. Neurons, or brain cells, align structurally in the brain to create superhighway systems called neural networks. The place where neurons meet is called the synaptic gap. Within this gap, electrical impulses leap from one neuron to the next, facilitated by neurotransmitters (chemical messengers). Some neurotransmitters you might find familiar are serotonin, dopamine, cortisol, and norepinephrine.

Depression is caused by insufficient amounts of one or more neurotransmitters (usually serotonin and/or dopamine). Serotonin is the neurotransmitter that allows you to feel calm and content. Dopamine is the neurotransmitter that allows you to feel excited and interested. When these are imbalanced, information does not move through the superhighway system efficiently or effectively.

Medications (anti-depressants: Prozac, Zoloft, Paxil) can restore this chemical imbalance in most people. Along with medication, cognitive-behavioral therapy can help those who are suffering depression-related

Looking back, I think Cameron exhibited every symptom of depression. I wish the therapists I took him to (five in all) had done a more thorough examination of his psyche and family history. They should have known that asking a teenager how he felt would not be answered truthfully, and his answers would not be helpful in his own treatment. A couple of Cameron's therapists admitted that Cameron knew how to answer their questions so they would release him from therapy.

Collecting a thorough family history might have told them much more than he told them. I have a grandfather who completed suicide, another grandfather who suffered from depression and was an alcoholic, an uncle who suffered from depression and abused pain meds, and a half-brother who to this day fights his own demons. The therapists didn't ask him or me, he didn't tell, and I didn't realize I needed to share this information.

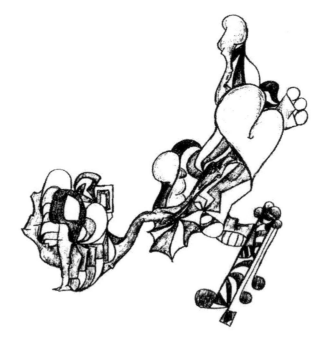

trauma and grief. This twofold treatment is a best practice in helping anyone who suffers from depression.

Depression has a strong **genetic** component, meaning it is passed down through relatives on one or both sides of the family. A genetic predisposition does not mean you'll develop depression, but it's a strong possibility, especially if you're experiencing negative environmental stress. A genetic predisposition leads to differences in how the brain functions and responds to stress –some people naturally handle stress much better than others.

Temperamental traits also contribute to a person's propensity for depression: low adaptability, insecure attachment, lack of approachability, low activity level, pessimistic (quitter) attitude.

Depression can also be caused by outside influences. Alcohol abuse, use of sedatives, barbiturates, narcotics, or prescription medication can cause imbalances in brain chemistry (neurotransmitters) that can result in depression. Diseases and the degenerative effects of aging can also be contributing factors.

Cameron's dad was adopted, so I didn't know if there were mental health issues in his birth family. However, his adoptive mom was a seriously disturbed person. We know from research on mother-infant interactions that a mother's personality and disposition contribute significantly to the wiring of her baby's brain. Interestingly, when I look back at photos of Cameron's dad, he was rarely smiling. He was a good dad in many ways but he had some problems, too.

I know saying this implies that I perhaps was not a good mother, but I assure you I was a good enough parent. What I am stressing is the genetic component of depression and that sometimes, even with the best parenting, bad things can happen to your child.

Cameron's psychiatrist and I weren't sure if Cameron suffered from bipolar disorder. But his doctor said that bipolar is difficult to diagnose in an office setting. Had he lived with Cameron, perhaps he could have distinguished bipolar from drug abuse. Nonetheless, it became our shared goal to alert parents about the possibility of a bipolar condition and to remain vigilant for the signs.

90% of all suicides are committed by people suffering from some form of depression. Many, like Cameron, were under the care of a physician or mental health professional at the time of their suicide.

BIPOLAR DISORDER

More and more young people are being diagnosed with another type of depression called Bipolar Disorder (BD). BD used to be called manic depression and was considered an adult disorder. However, thanks to a greater understanding in the medical field of how brain disorders manifest in children, many children are receiving a BD diagnosis. Bipolar disorder, unlike depressive disorders, includes an occurrence of a manic episode. In other words, the sufferer experiences extreme highs and extreme lows. In children, this can look like hyperactivity with extensive tantrums, inability to self-soothe, and extreme and quick shifts in mood.

Bipolar Disorder in teens and adults is characterized by cycles of mixed periods of mania (extreme excitement) and of depression (extreme sadness). The cycles usually begin gradually, but are long-lasting (days or weeks) and can be dramatic. While in the manic state, a person is restless and unnaturally elated. They typically have an overabundance of confidence, energy, and can be very talkative.

A bipolar condition can cause the sufferers to take excessive risks and make imprudent decisions that can have humiliating or damaging consequences. They will often have a feeling of invincibility, an increased sexual desire, grandiose thinking and ideas, and a decreased need for sleep. During a manic episode, as you can imagine, the person is unable to work and socialize normally.

The causes of Bipolar Disorder can be similar to those for depression: biochemical and/or genetic. However, a person will not develop BD from

At 15, Cameron was prescribed Wellbutrin for depression by our family doctor. However, it made him feel zombie-like. His psychiatrist prescribed Lexapro. Lexapro alone did not relieve his symptoms. Cameron was prescribed Abilify: this drug is an antipsychotic medication used to treat the symptoms of schizophrenia and manic or mixed (manic and depressive) episodes of Bipolar Disorder. Lexapro and Abilify combined seemed to help Cameron function normally. Unfortunately, by age 16 Cameron was also self-medicating with a variety of drugs and alcohol and was exhibiting some very quirky behaviors.

a normal life crisis or bereavement. Bipolar Disorder starts with a genetic and/or biological predisposition that is typically triggered by a life stressor (gene-environment interaction) but can also be activated spontaneously.

Bipolar Disorder is NOT schizophrenia, which involves hallucinations and incoherence lasting for a week or more. However, without treatment, BD may progress into psychosis (loss of contact with reality). Bipolar Disorder and depression share the same treatments: medication, therapy, and a support network. Substance abuse can make the symptoms of bipolar worse and can interfere with recovery.

Five or more of these symptoms suggest a manic episode:

- Racing speech and thoughts
- Decreased need for sleep
- Elevated mood and exaggerated optimism
- Increased mental and physical activity
- Excessive irritability, aggressive behavior, and impatience
- Poor judgment
- Reckless behavior (excessive spending, rash decisions, erratic driving)
- Difficulty concentrating
- Inflated sense of self-importance
- Excessive involvement in pleasurable activities (e.g., buying spree, drug abuse, sex)
- Destructive
- Increased interest in goal activity – will get what they need or want no matter what

life is like a big ass tree
born with courage
then as you get older,
it begins to flee
born complaining and whining
helpless to the world
taught to be afraid of what you
think
you'll learn better one day
you say
but will you?
paranoia of authority will control
you
this will go away one day
you say
but will it?
born with nothing to fear except
everything
don't give a fuck what people
think
then the drop beings
falling to the earth
isn't gravity a bitch?

but will the branches be weak
enough to let you keep falling
or will you hit that hard branch?
you know one of those big bitches
that kill you instantly.
never.
luck is against you.
snapping more and more as you
go.
getting harder to breath
why won't you stop grabbing for
branches and accept the truth?
eyes watering and you see your
future
then you've reached your final
goal in life
you don't get any rewards for
this one
laying on the hard, cold earth
it's so peaceful now
no more lies
silence

Depression and Bipolar Disorder contribute to teen suicide and should be treated quickly and aggressively. If you are not the parent but suspect a teen is struggling, notify the parents. Keep in mind that parents don't always think clearly when their child is troubled. Have phone numbers ready for them and provide guidance and support.

People with Bipolar Disorder may need your assistance to get the help they need. When in a manic state they don't want to be helped because they think they feel great and are invincible.

CAMERON's spiral into depression

Cameron was a deep thinker, intense and emotional. One evening Cameron went into the kitchen, got a bagel, put his favorite strawberry cream cheese on it and then decided to have a heart-to-heart with me in the family room. Cameron declared that he wanted to move out and knew how he could live out of his car. This was quite far-fetched but I suppose, in a teenager's mind, it was plausible.

I asked about taking showers, eating, sleeping – all the normal functions that occur when you live in a brick and mortar house. He said he would depend on friends. I don't remember all his great ideas on the topic, but at some point reason won out and he thought perhaps living in his car was not the best idea. Further into the conversation, he said he had a lot to say to the world and wanted to be heard. He felt strongly about this and got so excited that he absentmindedly swung his bagel around, splattering strawberry cream cheese on the wall (when packing to move out of that house, we still found pink spots on the wall). Cameron became so embroiled in the discussion he ended up on the floor crying saying he just wanted to be heard. He had a brilliant mind but unfortunately didn't know how to tame it.

THREE

Teen Depression

Teen depression may not feel very different from adult depression. However, teens do experience different risk factors from adults and may have different symptoms. In addition, teens may be more vulnerable to depression because (a) developmentally, their brains are not as sophisticated as an adult's brain, (b) they lack the freedom of movement and independence that adults possess (e.g., trapped at school or in their home lives), and (c) they lack access to resources that are readily available to adults (money, professionals, support systems).

Risk Factors

Stressful events can trigger sadness and/or fear, but when teens can't move past the event, or get control of their emotions, depression may creep into their lives. What kinds of events put a teen at risk for developing depression? Let's explore some of the most obvious.

Relationships can be very problematic for teenagers, particularly intense romantic relationships with quick starts and turbulent endings. Teenagers are not experienced in managing relationships, moderating their own emotions or accurately reading the emotions of others. Most teens eventually figure out that after a breakup things will usually turn out okay, that there's hope, and everything will sort itself out. But some teens don't have the ability to realize life will indeed go on and that they will survive the hurt the breakup caused.

So I sit with a decision again
wondering how many times I
should lie not to the girls,
but myself,
about all the times that I try.
I know I attempt, for some
reason I hope, about having a
perfect us.
Sometimes I'd rather hang from
a rope about 4 feet off the
ground than having to deal with
emotion.
But they possess power and glee
and all else.
They carry some heart-choking
notion. Both make me happy, yet
still a little shady, and both are
specimens of my ideal lady.
Both blond underneath, yet
sporting brown or red,
the queen of "the girls" changes
weekly instead
But is their hair dead?...no, but
weak,
 just as they portray
themselves.
But they lie, so humans do
indeed. I accept their lies, or
minor quirks, or even their
insane obsessions.
But only a fool, in his idiocy,
wouldn't learn his lesson. Though
the one I want is days away,
 I still put myself through hell.
But it's amazing that such
creatures of havoc could ever
make me feel so well.
It's like a sinning touch that
gives so much, but always leaves
me insane.
Some use abuse, yet till I choose
which one is least a pain.

Unfortunately, often parents cannot recollect the deep emotions they once felt as teenagers. I remember breaking up with a boyfriend, but I don't remember all the feelings that went along with it. I'm sure they were monumental at the time. I'm sure I felt hurt when I was dumped. But when recalling it now, I think I just brushed myself off and got back up on the horse. That's what we tell our children to do because we know that this too shall pass. We wish they would listen to us, but that's not how they feel – and they feel everything!

Don't discount or gloss over a **breakup** with a girlfriend or boyfriend as something your teen will bounce back from quickly. That's rarely the case. They feel the hurt deeply and need to work through the emotions. If the pain is unbearable, then your teen may slip into clinical depression. Don't expect them to share their feelings because they may not understand them themselves. Instead, they may act angry, sullen, critical or negative as a cover for their sadness and fears.

The **death** of a parent or close friend will naturally cause a grief reaction but can also lead to depression. The difference between grief and depression is your frame of mind rather than the stressful event itself. When grieving you can manage your sadness, you can function, you can talk to others about how sad you feel and you can talk yourself out of being sad when you need to. With depression you cannot talk yourself out of it and find it difficult to talk to others about how you are feeling. You can't rid yourself of negative thoughts or feelings and you have trouble carrying out your everyday activities. When a teen loses a parent or close friend (or pet), they will naturally grieve, but they may not necessarily fall into a deep depression. However, it's best to be aware that it could happen and to be prepared for an early intervention.

Cameron would often come home from school and ask that we not bother him because he had a bad day. He said he was tired of talking to people and only wanted to get in his bed and sleep. If a conflict occurred, even on the weekend, he would head off to his bed and stay there for many, many hours. I would check in on him and often find him in his bed, not sleeping - just cuddled up in his many blankets.

Cameron's sleep habits were not habits at all. He stopped sleeping normally when he was 16. We tried to enforce "normal" sleep patterns like a set to-bed and to-rise time, but when you're depressed, sleep doesn't come automatically. He would stay up most of the night blogging, listening to music, drawing, playing games, hanging out in chat rooms, or working on design projects on his computer. Yet he always got up in the morning and was ready to go to school. Cameron rarely asked to stay home from school. It seemed his life was at school.

When the weekend rolled around he would stay in bed the entire weekend. During his last summer, he wanted to sleep during weekdays, too. We could not tolerate our son laying in the bed all day, so we implemented a rule that he would have to be up by 1:00 p.m. and out of the house looking for a job. He hated this. We discovered later that he would go to a friend's house and go back to sleep.

I think that I want to sleep before school comes to an end. I just don't want to be awake anymore. I'm feeling depressed again. Damn. I think I want food too. Meh, I can live without that. But staying awake too long reveals too much reality. This making sleep essential to human survival. Stupid sleep.

Divorce is another risk factor for teens. When parents divorce, kids must go along with the decision because they have no say in the matter. This may include a move into a new house, a new school, and perhaps living with a step-parent for the first time. Even without divorce, just changing schools can be a major stressful event in a teen's life. Teens feel these changes more acutely than adults and have fewer coping skills to deal with them.

Crazy sleep patterns can result in depression. Teens these days have far too many distractions – cell phones, TVs in their rooms, texting, IMing, video games. They stay up late entertaining themselves with these gadgets, and sometimes text each other at all hours of the night about some drama that is unfolding. Then they're sleepy when they get to class and don't perform as well in school. They come home and take afternoon naps; they sleep late on weekends to make up for sleep lost during the week. These irregular sleep patterns are very harmful to the body and the brain. Teens need about 9 hours of sleep each night to function best, but most teens do not get enough sleep — a study by the Sleep Foundation found that only 15% reported sleeping 8 1/2 hours on school nights.

Lately we are hearing more and more about **bullying** in our schools. It has become so bad that some states have created legislation in an effort to stop this torment that plagues children and teens. The National Education Association found that everyday 160,000 U.S. children miss school due to fear of attacks or intimidation by peers; 24% of high school children say they took a weapon to school at least once in the past year for self-protection. And 73% of 10- to 18-year-olds hit someone during the year because they were angry. Children who are not liked by their classmates and/or who are under attack by a bully can become

Teen Depression

The soft side of Cameron loved soft-touch fabrics, children and cuddly animals. Yet there was a flip side to all this softness – Cameron loved to fight. After the movie Fight Club came out, he and his friends would go to a park and fight – weekly. Even the girls would join in. I could not fathom this and often told him that he should not be beating on his friends and especially the girls, but he said that the girls enjoyed it, too. I can see how some pent-up emotions could be released by fighting, but why not something else? I hated that insane activity!

Cameron had an argument with one of his girlfriends that turned into a physical fight. He said he knocked her down on the ground and then kicked her really hard in the butt. She said that she had a concussion after that and was in a lot of pain but did not want any harm to come to Cameron. She also hit Cameron, so it was not a one-sided fight, mind you. She told me that she started it. I hate telling the world that my son hit other people, but we can't save teens unless we tell the truth about depression and substance abuse.

Lonely nights with you in my mind.
every thought hurts me.
all the truths begin to unwind,
but there's no jealousy.
I want to break your nose
I want to crush your hopes
I want to chase you with a knife,
we all know how that story goes
but I really, really, really want to take your life.

depressed. What's worse, some kids have been known to take their lives because they could not tolerate or stop the bullying they had to endure at school.

Teens may act as if they don't want or need parental attention. But teens can feel **neglected** when parents have many responsibilities to tend to (working long hours, single parenting, limited financial resources, several children to care for, caring for aging parents). Yes, teens are ideally supposed to grow up, spread their wings, and soar, but they don't always make the right decisions in the process of growing up. In reality they need parental guidance as much now as when they were five years old. If they don't receive what they need for a long enough period of time, bad things can happen, including depression.

Relationship violence can also trigger depression in teenagers. A girl goes on a date and ends up getting raped. A boy and girl are dating and he is demanding more sexual activity than she is willing to do. She doesn't want to lose her boyfriend, so she goes along with his demands. care about, and who they think care about them. When a teen can't navigate out of the relationship, he can become depressed.

Witnessing violence, either at home or in the neighborhood, can trigger depression in teens. A teen has to endure watching his mom get beat up by his dad and he doesn't know how to stop it. A teen is exposed to ongoing gang-related violence and he feels helpless and scared. These children did not choose to be a witness to violence, nor to be trapped by

Untitled Poem

Whimsical toss by the waterfall.
Secular ways of the breeze.
Irrational, offset and screwed
As her fingers bounce from the keys.
With a crash into a solid brick wall,
And screaming at top of my lung
The night's chaos finally unwinding,
But the misery only begun.
Her tears flowing on, everlasting,
Realization of what I proposed.
And now I fear my subconscious,
Whose wicked actions arose.
I am not very violent at all;
Neither malice nor tyrannical hate.
Though I laid ravenous hands upon her,
I hope love won't arrive too late.
I love without question or comment
But always with a delicate whisper.
And never again shall I touch that child
(continued)

life circumstances where there is no relief. Teens who can't escape these abusive situations can end up becoming depressed.

Symptoms of Teen Depression

Your teen may not know that he is depressed. Most people don't. It takes a professional to determine a diagnosis of depression. You can ask your teen about his feelings, but if your teen won't talk to you about what's bothering him, there are some symptoms you can look for that may indicate depression. If you see any of these symptoms in your teen, consider it a red flag and start seeking help. Keep in mind that treating the depression as opposed to the symptom(s) may be your first line of defense.

Drug Use

Teens suffering from depression will often find that illicit drugs or prescription medications (often stolen) will temporarily erase their sadness and create a false sense of relief and even happiness. This cycle of depression and self-medication is very dangerous and extremely difficult to break. Using the wrong drugs can cause addiction, withdrawal symptoms and can magnify the underlying problem.

Physical Symptoms

Many teens complain of **physical ailments** and they often do experience growing pains from normal development. Pain itself is enough to make someone depressed but depression can cause physical pain as well. Teens suffering from depression will have more intense and persistent

Unless she allow that I kiss her.

So sweet her touch, and delicate,

Like rose petal upon one's lips.

And so calm her voice, it soothes my mind,

Causing reality to slip.

I don't know why I harmed this girl . . .

No reason yet discovered.

Yet I hope she will forgive and believe me

When I say I love her.

(written after a brick wall car accident with girlfriend, followed by a night in jail due to a warrant for his arrest for ignoring a court date.)

physical complaints than typical ones, such as headaches, stomachaches, backaches, muscle fatigue, or feeling tired all the time. In addition, no amount of aspirin, ibuprofen or other pain relievers will cure their ailments.

Noticeable **weight loss or gain** can be a symptom of depression. It might be difficult to attribute weight changes to depression because a teen's weight tends to fluctuate with the ebb and flow of hormones. But if it's a drastic change – that's not normal. Watch for obsession with food, or complete lack of interest in food, plus lack of enjoyment of their favorite foods, and/or shunning food-based functions (e.g., Thanksgiving, cookouts, family meals). Not all food issues are symptoms of eating disorders or depression – medication can cause appetite increases or decreases. But all food issues should be addressed because proper nutrition is essential to healthy adolescent development.

Self-injury is another cry for help by a depressed teen. Self-mutilation or self-injury is a means of inflicting controlled pain when controlling the mental pain of depression is impossible. Self-injury usually is an impulsive, repetitive act. Teens may become upset or triggered by an event, and an urge to hurt themselves emerges as a way to control what is not controllable. At other times self-injury is a planned event, inflicted in a controlled, methodical manner. Cutting is the most common form of self-injury; it may be painful or not, depending on the person's state of mind at the time. It involves making cuts or scratches with a sharp object or irritating the skin with a blunt object such as an eraser until it is raw or

REAL VISIONS

This is a graphic design project Cameron created regarding depression awareness. To the right of the drawing are the facts Cameron researched. In the box below, Cameron describes the design aspects of his drawing.

-Depression involves thoughts about death, negative thoughts about oneself, a sense of worthlessness, a sense of hopelessness that things could get better, low energy, and noticeable changes in appetite or sleep.

-Consider these statistics about teen suicide and teen depression: about 1% of all teens attempts suicide and about 1% of those suicide attempts results in death (that means about 1 in 10,000 teens dies from suicide).

Nearly four percent of the boys (3.7 percent) and over six percent of the girls (6.3 percent) reported PTSD symptoms during the preceding six months, indicating that a high percentage of youth in the United States encounter traumatic events and experience significant emotional responses associated with these events

By blacking out the eyes and making the facial features scarce, it makes it easier to replace them with yourself. The grunge and splatter also subconciously reinforce the idea of suicide and depression.

bleeds. The arms and legs are usually the target areas where most fresh cuts or scars can be hidden.

More typical of girls than boys, some girls have cutting parties where they teach each other how to cut. Be on the lookout for knives, razorblades, and scissors in your teen's bedroom (and backpack) as well as wearing long sleeve shirts when the temperature dictates short sleeves or wearing wide bracelets to hide scarring.

Other forms of self-injury include burning, poisoning, overdosing, carving words or symbols on the skin, head banging, pinching, piercing the skin with sharp objects, biting, pulling out hair and interfering with wound healing. This is not a suicide attempt, although death may be a result if taken too far. Instead, these are attempts to control pain.

If you discover your teen is practicing self-injury, consult your family doctor or a mental health professional immediately. Cutting can be addictive and difficult to stop. It's a very dangerous practice!

Emotional (Affective) Symptoms

Your teen seems to have an **irrational negative self-concept**. Your teen feels guilty about events he has no control over (e.g., death of a loved one). Your teen feels embarrassed about being seen in public. Your teen is bright and capable but doesn't feel worthy of praise. These negative, irrational feelings can be signs of depression. My son was a talented graphic design artist as well as photographer, but he did not believe in himself or trust his skills even after winning in local competitions. He, indeed, suffered from depression.

Cameron asked if we would remove his bed frame so he'd be closer to the floor with just the box springs and mattress on the floor. I agreed because that didn't seem to harm anything. Cameron always looked so comfortable lying in his bed. He would have two or three blankets that he loved and a couple of stuffed animals to hug as well as a regular pillow or two. He enjoyed it when I washed his clothes with fabric softener. He liked the softness of the world, not the sharp edges he often had to deal with.

But he also enjoyed breaking things. He told me that he wanted to break plates, anything. Cameron had a photography assignment where he was to photograph an egg in different places. I drove him around the area for this photo shoot and when he was done, he asked, "Can I break the eggs now?" I figured that the cost of eggs was minimal to the pleasure Cameron was probably going to gain from breaking them. He enjoyed breaking those eggs in empty parking lots and on the sides of vacant buildings.

If your teen has a prolonged, persistent sad mood and **has lost** the ability to experience **pleasure**, he is likely depressed. How sad for a teen to not experience pleasure in their friends and family, the joy of holding a puppy or kitten, the delight of hearing new music. When the thrill is gone, a teen may think there is nothing more to live for.

Depression may follow when feelings of **anger, worry and anxiety** persist for longer than two weeks with no resolution. We all feel frustrated and mad sometimes, but most people are able to analyze why they feel this way and to resolve the problems. For example, when the holidays roll around, I find myself starting to feel mad at the world. Inevitably, I ask myself, "Why am I feeling so angry?" I now realize that the holidays stir up a lot of sadness for me because I miss spending time with Cameron. I understand and accept this reaction and I take steps to manage my emotions such as talking to my therapist and spending time with my friends and family. Teens don't have the ability to ask and answer the "Why am I feeling this way?" question or to seek out helpful resources. When a teen appears angry at the world for days on end but doesn't know why, he's definitely at risk.

Overreaction to correction or criticism is another clue to suspect depression. We know teens can be touchy about many subjects but being consistently overly touchy implies a bigger problem. For example, you catch your daughter leaving the house wearing an extremely low-cut, see-though blouse. When you stop her, she screams at you for being mean, runs to her room crying and doesn't come out for the rest of the evening. You may interpret this behavior as pushing the limits, and it may be. But her overreaction is an indicator of depression if this is atypical of her temperament or when other symptoms of depression are present. If you

There was once a time when a few of my friends wanted to destroy Christmas. There were baseball bats, golf clubs and mass amounts of speed. I wasn't too thrilled with the possible outcome, but alas, I did it anyways. We didn't get caught, but if so, it could have been very bad. So... yeah.

1. I suppose that the first would have benefitted from the second. The more, the merrier. And that's what Christmas is all about.
2. The advice was definitely bad. Nobody benefitted as far as the community went.
3. Of course, I would do it again. Though risky and rather illegal, it was probably the best Christmas fiasco ever.

(This appears to have been written for an English assignment, 12th grade)

Arguing with you over what type of clothes to wear is NOT in and of itself a sign of depression – that's normal teen rebellion.

find that everything you say to your teen is met with an argument or highly emotional response, you may want to have her evaluated by a mental health professional.

Suicidal thoughts or actions are scary to acknowledge. Clues include written items turned in at school, or poetry you find at home describing how miserable the child feels, or artwork that is very disturbing (images of guns pointed at a head, a rope tied in a noose, blood – you get the idea). Some teens will actually say, "I'll just kill myself" during even minor family arguments. It is important that you ask your teen if they are seriously thinking about suicide and if they have a plan; there's a difference in the state of mind of a teen who blurts out threats versus one who has an actual plan. They may be relieved that you noticed how bad they feel and admit their unhappiness. If that's the case, locate a mental health professional as soon as possible. Don't put it off! Call one of the numbers listed in the back of the book for help.

Poor School Performance

Any **fluctuation of grades** on report cards can be an indicator of how your teen is doing mentally and emotionally. When A's and B's become D's and F's, depression, drug use, or maybe a combination of the two could be the culprit. A drop in grades could also indicate an inability to concentrate. Too often this is attributed to ADHD, but it could very well be depression. Skipping classes or truancy can also be an indicator. Suddenly your son is **getting in trouble** with other students and his teachers, and is being sent to the principal's office. Maybe he's getting in trouble for smoking cigarettes when he knows he's not of legal age or when he's on school property. Parents are likely to punish these

JULY 21, 2005

When there's no reason to run,
walking seems so pointless.
Why progress when the present
position is so perfect?
Uncomfortably perfect.
Perfectly uncomfortable.

Why can't I be happy anymore?
There are so many things I
feel no reason to live for.
So many things I hate... but
is knowing that there are
still things I love a good
enough reason to be here?

I just want to be happy again.

Kelly was the reason I wanted to live...
now she's the reason I want not to.

behaviors. But if thumbing his nose at authority is actually a cry for attention to an underlying problem, then punishing your teen for these behaviors may not work. If this is the case, consider depression as the cause instead of defiance or entitlement, and seek professional help.

Changes in Daily Routines or Interests

If your son usually comes home from school and starts playing **video games** but now doesn't, you have to wonder, why the change? Sure, it made you crazy that he played so much, but you need to question why the sudden change. If your daughter loved to talk on the phone till all hours of the night and suddenly **the phone** is quiet – why this change? When your teen pulls away and isolates herself from her usual **friends** – what's happening? Teens **sleeping** till noon on the weekends is a given but what if your teen comes home from school and goes straight to bed. My son did just that on a number of occasions. Changes in daily routines can be early warning signs for potential mental health issues. It's okay to ask questions; the answers can give you clues to their mental well being. For example, sometimes my son would say, "Don't talk to me, I've had a bad day." Sometimes he would share a rational reason for his irritability. But usually he'd say he was tired of people in general. How do you respond to that?

Music choices can be revealing, too. There is a powerful connection between music and our feelings and thoughts, which is probably why music plays a vital part in most teens' lives. It's common to see teens walking around with earbuds and cords attached to their heads listening

Music could always be heard streaming from Cameron's room. He would play CDs on his alarm clock/radio/CD player until he discovered he could get more sound from the speakers connected to his PC. So he started playing CDs on his computer as well as downloading songs when that became popular. I find it ironic that Cameron totally missed the iPod craze by just one year. He would have had no problem filling up one after another with tunes.

Cameron's music choices did change along with the severity of his depression. Up until he was 15, Cameron listened to Sting and similar music. When he was 16, he discovered the Dead Kennedys (a hardcore punk band) and went on to acquire all of their CDs. As the depression and substance abuse took over, his music switched to even harder Punk bands (or to my mind) such as Rancid, NOFX, and Sublime These bands seemed to scream rather than soothe. After Cameron died, one of his friends told me that he'd been listening to Led Zeppelin II over and over. I had never thought of that album (in my era at least) as being depressing, but it is very much so.

Remember, depression is a disease that requires medical treatment. It cannot and should not be brushed under the rug.

to music. Parents need to stay cognizant of their teen's music choices. If you're not sure, you can stand outside their bedroom and listen to the music within. Or, playfully pull a sneak attack, pop out one of their earbuds and take a listen for yourself. If your teen gets upset because he doesn't want you to hear what he's listening to, or if what you hear is heartless, dreary or dismal sounding, be concerned that he is already depressed or could become depressed by the music.

If this same music choice continues for longer than two weeks question your teen about how he's feeling. Suggest your teen switch over to some happy music to improve his mood. If he claims the music isn't affecting him, pull up sites on the Internet that discuss how some types of music foster depression while others are used as a therapeutic tool to lift depression and anxiety and share it with him.

THE ULTIMATE LOVE LETTER

The Monkey says:

"You Suck!"

your love makes me
want to dive headfirst
into a pool of
razor blades.

I compare my
love for you to
an enema: unusual
and uncomfortable.

life without love
is impossible...
   DAMNIT!

everyone needs
someone. kinda like
everyone needs a
bullet to the
head

FOUR

Addictions

"My lover was cold and cruel and hardly faithful, but I never
fell out of love. Every time I see a movie in which people
are doing coke, I want it. I can almost taste it in the back of
my throat. I still love that taste. You don't get over the
drugs, you don't ever fall out of love." *Patti Davis, daughter
of president Ronald Reagan*

When Patti Davis wrote this, she'd been sober for a long period of time so there's a poignancy to her vulnerability. She said that it was no accident she was using romance language to describe her addiction. She went on to say that her addiction was a "very profound, positive, appetitive, chocolate croissant, wanna-have-it, sexual object" kind of thing.

The HBO documentary film, "Addiction," reveals addictions start before the age of 20. Therefore it is urgent that parents and others address a developing substance abuse problem as early as possible. Don't assume a child will grow out of their issues (rebellion, experimentation, etc.). Rather, a child may grow into an adult addict. Teens are more susceptible to developing addictions than adults because of how the brain develops.

1. The prefrontal cortex located above the eyes acts to mediate the mid-brain. It is the rational, logical part of the brain that slows us down to think, stops impulsive behaviors, judges situations and evaluates the consequences of our actions.

CAROLYN's cigarette habit

I became addicted to nicotine/tobacco when I was 17. It took me quite a long time to realize that I must quit smoking. There were two things that finally made me quit: 1) I did it for Cameron in hopes of getting him to quit smoking cigarettes (which failed) and 2) there was an ad on TV and in print that showed a woman who had lung cancer saying that it is the most painful thing you can imagine. I could feel her pain because I had a couple of bouts of pleurisy during my 20s. Pleurisy is an inflammation of the lining surrounding the lungs; every breath you take hurts so badly that you wish you didn't have to breathe again. I didn't want to experience the pain of lung cancer.

I don't want it anymore.

Not your bullshit.

Not your smile.

Not your idiocy.

Not you...

Let me take the wrong path.

2. Teen's prefrontal cortex is underdeveloped and does not always respond with "stop" signals.

3. Lacking this "stop" signal, along with a desire to try new things, teens will experiment with drugs not realizing that what they are doing might actually be bad or harmful or could have long-term effects.

4. Late adolescence is the peak time for developing dependence on alcohol and tobacco. "Addiction is a disorder of young people" (Dr. Mark Willenbring). Between the ages of 15-25 the brain goes through massive reorganization in its structure and function. The weakness of a teen's brain at this time is volatile thinking and poor coping skills. As a result teens tend to experience stress acutely and fail to see solutions. Throwing a drug into the mix that makes them feel numb, or euphoric, omnipotent, or untouchable by life's daily grind prevents them from learning stress-coping and problem-solving skills.

If a person becomes addicted to drugs and/or alcohol in their teens, they typically fail to mature beyond adolescence. They grow older but emotionally and socially they act and think like a teenager. And they will not begin to progress until they get clean. Those teens who put off drug, alcohol, and tobacco use until after age 18 are significantly less likely to develop an addiction than those who experiment prior to age 18.

After I quit smoking, cigarettes were banned in the house, but Cameron was quite creative in fueling his addiction to cigarettes. We set a security alarm every evening before going to bed, mostly so Cameron would not sneak out of the house and get into trouble. He learned that he could not open his bedroom window without setting the alarm off. So he discovered the storage space in the game room and smoked in there until we found his cigarette butts. We changed the doorknob to a locking one. Next, he turned to the attic to smoke, which we didn't know about until after his death. That's one reason he was in the attic the morning of his death – to smoke cigarettes. Yet another reason to get your teens to quit smoking – you don't know what it will lead to. I'm not saying that my son died from suicide because he smoked cigarettes, but smoking certainly led him to try other drugs.

Cameron used other drugs including alcohol. He would drink alcohol before going to school in the morning. He bragged about his drinking and partying in a letter he sent to a friend whose mother discovered the letter and called to warn me. I'm sure this was before he tried meth. Cameron did many risky behaviors while under the influence of drugs and alcohol. Thrill seeking for Cameron was skateboarding on the roof of a car – presumably when it was not moving – and breaking and entering into vacant homes.

An alcoholic's risk of taking his life is 50 to 70 percent higher than the general population. (Centers for Disease Control & Prevention)

FIVE

Methamphetamine – the Devil's Drug

I included a chapter on the illegal substance methamphetamine (meth) for many reasons. The most important reason is that meth was Cameron's drug of choice and I therefore have a lot of experience and knowledge of the drug's effect on a teen. Another reason is that meth is highly and immediately addictive, one of the most destructive drugs to the brain and body, and, unfortunately, affordable and accessible.

The History of Methamphetamine

Methamphetamine is a variation of amphetamine. Both are stimulants to the central nervous system but methamphetamine is stronger, has a higher addictive quality, and more physical consequences. It is believed the first amphetamine produced was by a German chemist in the late 1880's. This early form was used as a nasal decongestant for asthma sufferers. But soon its side effects of alertness, energy, and euphoria were realized. It's rumored that Adolph Hitler was addicted to methamphetamine, which likely contributed to his delusions of world domination and desire for racial cleansing. Amphetamines are notoriously used by soldiers: Japanese kamikaze pilots used it during WWII in order to stay awake for their missions and soldiers in the trenches use it to keep alert while involved in enemy lookouts and to feel immune to the horrors of war.

CAMERON's *drug use*

Meth was not Cameron's first drug to abuse; he smoked cigarettes, drank alcohol to excess, abused cold medications and pain meds, smoked marijuana, and I'm not sure what else he used before becoming addicted to meth. He admitted at one point during his stay in an outpatient rehab facility that meth was his drug of choice above all others.

Denial is Hope.

During the 1960s, doctors regularly prescribed Dexedrine and Benzedrine, forms of amphetamines, to women so they could stay thin and active. Long- distance truck drivers have taken amphetamine (or speed) for years; it keeps them wakeful for long periods of time, which allows them to complete more trips, thus achieving higher incomes.

During the 1970s speed freaks came were everywhere. Taking and injecting amphetamine was as popular as smoking marijuana. Amphetamines became illegal in the United States under the passage of the U.S. Drug Abuse Regulation and Control Act of 1970; yet up until then over 10 billion tablets of amphetamines or methamphetamine were produced and distributed.

Making Meth

Unfortunately, meth is easy to make and easy to buy, The cost of a gram of meth can be as low as $20. This small amount of money is easily attainable by the average teen. If they receive money for school lunches, they can go to school and buy meth instead. They don't have the desire to eat while under the influence of meth, so lunch is a moot point to a meth user.

There are many different recipes for manufacturing meth, but they all include ephedrine, pseudoephedrine, or phenylpropanolamine. These chemicals can be found in over-the-counter (OTC) medications (e.g., diet aids, cough, cold and allergy products). Meth "cooks" create meth in

(From Cameron's journal of his last writings)

Friday am   3:20 – midst of drug run for Kevin...

          9:10 – car has broken down...battery. Now we're stilling at Sara's. .   We dropped off Keith's shit to him & his brother. Pretty interesting group of people...they seemed to look up to me; not only for retrieving skat, but they "marveled" at my knowledge of the drug. Kevin's brother seemed to be somewhat fond of me...I'm happy about that if nothing else. He said he's from Garland. Apparently, he has a pretty perpetual contact for "smurf dope" as well. Hells yeah...

"labs" using these chemicals along with some other highly volatile ingredients (e.g., anti-freeze, alcohol, paint thinner, Freon, Red Devil lye, drain cleaner, and battery acid). Each of these products is legal, but when used to make meth the results can be devastating.

Meth labs can be found anywhere: homes, cars, hotel rooms, and storage facilities. Although making meth is easy and affordable, the risks are great. Explosions, fires, and chemical burns are common both externally and internally (inhaling the fumes can blister the lungs). Even the residual waste is toxic.

According to DEA El Paso Intelligence Center (EPIC), meth lab seizures throughout the U.S. have decreased since their all time high of 17,356 seizures in 2003 to 6,783 in 2008. The astounding decrease in labs is attributed to the Combat Methamphetamine Epidemic Act of 2005, which regulated the sale of OTC medication used in manufacturing methamphetamine.

> *Another common active ingredient found in many cough medications is dextromethorphan (DXM). Taking extremely large doses of DXM can get you high and many teens abuse these medications* for that reason.

(Entry from Cameron's journal of his last writings)

I'm totally going to college soon. Given, it is NCTC…still. Fuckin' college, man. Where did all those years go? Crazy aging process we humans have. Not a ton of animals live to be 100. I wonder what tortoises must think as they finally become over-the-hill at age 150. Wow…that topic changed rather quickly.

Anyways, I'm all ancy like a schoolgirl to start at NCTC. What fun, what knowledge, what mayhem will I stumble upon? I finally get to start over again. What greater honor is there than a resurrection? Finally an open window to meet new people, learn new things, and to truly be who I am without having to regret my actions.

Another thing that is "tickling" me; it kicks ass being 18. It's as if in all the previous years, I was kicked aside by older people. My opinions and outlooks constantly mocked. I'm free now…you may know more than me & have lived longer, but that doesn't make you wiser (<u>wisdom</u>—the application of knowledge). So fuck you if you disregard my inputs but it will always be there…never unspoken, never sugar-coated. I'm open to new ideas… are you?

Just last night, I gave advice to a thirty-two year-old man…one with a gun. When I spoke, he looked at me and listened. If I can influence an armed meth-junkie, I think I can influence anyone (except politicians and hairstylists (they're in a world of their own)).

Oh, shit. I left my cell phone at the house. Gotta go get that…supremely important, it is. I'll hit this up again in a little bit. Hfn.

Meth is the reason you now have to supply your ID when purchasing certain allergy and cold medications. While home labs have been greatly reduced in the U.S., the usage of meth has not. The illicit use of meth is now worldwide and it's a bumper crop in countries such as Mexico and India. A steady stream of meth is regularly smuggled into the U.S.

How Meth Affects the Brain

The medical uses for amphetamine are limited to treating ADHD, obesity, and narcolepsy. Methamphetamine is never prescribed because it's considered too destructive a drug; there is no safe way of using meth. Users of this powerful drug experience an intense high that lasts as long as 12 hours. Compare that to cocaine, which typically lasts only 30 minutes.

When meth is smoked or snorted (inhaled through the nose) the neurotransmitters dopamine and norepinephrine flood the brain causing an intense "rush," particularly in the pleasure center of the brain. Concentration spikes and a euphoric high and a state of extreme happiness are produced. With continued abuse, the reward center of the brain stops responding; more meth is needed to experience the same euphoric state. Addiction to meth does not occur solely because of its pleasurable effect, however; the speed at which it is absorbed likely contributes to its addictive power.

Students "think" meth helps with studying because they can stay up all night feeling happy and alert -- and sometimes it does. However,

(Class assignment)

Penitence...for Lent!

So, apparently I have to give up some "habit", or some "luxury." Though I live pretty simply as it is, I'll give up gummy bears. I suppose. Not all candy, because I survive off pixi-sticks and smarties on the weekends. However, gummy bears are sinfully and magically delicious.

Now that I have this settled, I don't know how to accomplish it. Wait, no. That's a lie. I very simply won't eat them. Well that was fun.

I apologize that I can't get extremely "into" this topic...I'm not religious in even the tiniest sense and I don't believe in rebirth. Peoples' habits/addictions help define one's personality. Quitting something that makes someone "who they are" doesn't quite make sense to me.

Regardless, no gummy bears until Easter. Technically, it's not such a bad thing...I usually stock-pile on those gummy seraphs around Easter-time anyways.

...Uh, God bless! And no gummy bears!

extended use of meth has a boomerang effect, lowering attention span and causing difficulty in information processing (making wise choices, and deciding when and how to act). What's worse, excessive dopamine and norepinephrine can cause neuron cell damage (nerve endings are cut back and re-growth is limited) and neuron death, particularly in the frontal lobe area of the brain responsible for rational and analytic thinking. The frontal lobe area of the brain is undergoing a massive transformation in late adolescence and early adulthood. Losing vital brain cells at this time can result in lifelong consequences.

Physical and Behavioral Signs of Meth Use

The most common physical sign of meth use is **weight loss** that occurs quickly and for no apparent reason. A consistent user's face becomes gaunt and hollow-eyed. There is often heavy sweating and oily hair, which results in a unique body odor. Teens who experience acne will have an increased amount on their faces as well as on their bodies. Nausea and diarrhea can occur as well as binging on sweets.

An increase in **cavities**, especially along the gum line, is prevalent. Long-term users develop what is known as "meth mouth," meaning they often lose their teeth quickly. The American Dental Association states that meth mouth is caused by a combination of dry mouth, extended periods of poor oral hygiene, tooth grinding and clenching, and high consumption of highly sugared carbonated soft drinks; meth use, like other drugs that stimulate the sympathetic nervous system, causes decreased production of acid-fighting saliva and increased thirst, which is often quenched by sugary beverages.

Cameron made the decision to taken his life while he was under the influence of meth. I can't remember when I found this out but I had a suspicion he was abusing his favorite drug. This was confirmed on the autopsy report that we received a month later. Cameron had a very large amount of meth in his system at the time of his death. The only other drug present was his anti-depressant.

Sunday morning.... Back to my illness. It turns out that Lauren and Kelly had a plan to destroy me after the night they conversed. Lauren says that she didn't want to do it...yet if I would have gone to see her picture get taken, my demise would have been followed through with. Thought this didn't happen because I walked away from her, the thought that she would participate nags me still.

Basic struggling outcome: I don't know if I can trust either one of them. How can I not be under the assumption that they're plotting even now. It's as if falling in love is a conspiracy...and I get to play as the victim. The saddest part is that I don't have a "Brutus" to at least comfort me. For the longest time I trusted both of them...nevermore. At least, not to the same extent. It's a fucking travesty.

Fuck girls, fuck trust, and above all, fuck love. All a hideous montage of pain and helplessness. Fuck everything. I'm hating life again...fuck it.

Another contributing factor is likely the corrosive chemicals found in homemade batches of meth. (www.drugfree.org/meth360)

More Physical Signs

- Shortness of breath
- Nasal problems or nosebleeds
- Sores that do not heal
- Dilated pupils (under the influence of meth)
- Burns on lips or fingers
- Track marks on arms

Behavioral Signs

- Withdraws from the family and his usual friends
- Changes friends or peer groups
- No longer pursues previously favorite activities
- Activity level increases: twitching, shaking, scratching, or can't be still
- Repetitious behavior: picking at their skin, pulling out hair absentmindedly, compulsive cleaning or grooming
- Oddly disassembling and re-assembling objects (their computer or stereo)
- Unusually long periods of sleep (24-48 hours) or sleeplessness (24-120 hours)
- Incessant talking, irritability, aggression or violent behavior that is out of character
- Erratic attention span
- False sense of confidence and power
- Dishonesty and secretiveness

Wednesday

So, first day at a new job. Pretty boring, yet...promising.

Anyways...right now I'm running shit. Kelly and Lauren are both at Tony's. Alone. Who knows what they'll be talking about. Ever since Lauren told me about her and Kelly's plan to ruin me, I have been having trouble trusting either one. So, for the two to be together gossiping is really scaring me. Oh and how. I love them, but I'm seriously scared of both...

Why can't I fix this problem? Why is it that I can't simply say "no" to one of them? It's becoming a rather ripe pain in the ass. The saddest part is that I know I'm the one causing all this chaos. But there's nothing, it appears, that I can rightly do about it.

Now, Kelly's kicked out of her house without a cell phone. And, no, it's not my fault. Nothing that I did got her in any trouble. Yes I housed her...but my mother didn't catch her, I didn't tell on her and Blonde said that she had things covered. What part of that is my fault?

That's it. I can tell... my day is going to hell. Kelly has destroyed the day once again. Thank you, Kelly.

- Highly sexualized behavior (though you may not see this)
- Dangerous behavior (driving recklessly, challenging authority)

Mental problems include paranoia, anxiousness, nervousness, agitation and extreme moodiness that go beyond normal teen behavior. Severe depression can be a result of meth use, creating a vicious cycle. A teen may feel depressed, try meth and re-discover happiness. But when they come off a high, the resulting depression is worse than what they originally had. So they use again… and again.

Meth users can experience schizophrenic episodes such as hallucinations and delusions (e.g., parasites or insects crawling under their skin). In all cases of meth use, the user experiences a loss of inhibitions and feels totally in control. If you notice any combination of these symptoms, it is imperative that you explore your teen's room as well as their car, if they have one. There are several types of meth paraphernalia to look for.

Forms of Meth

1. Tabs – these are brightly colored and the size of a pencil eraser. They contain large amounts of caffeine as well as meth.
2. Powder – this is the most common form of meth. Users can snort powder up their noses, rub it on their gums, wrap it in cigarette paper and swallow or insert the wrapped powder into their anus. The powder quickly dissolves so it is sometimes added to coffee or alcoholic drinks. Powder can stay in the body 12 hours. Look for powder in the tiny plastic baggies.

We thought we could curtail his use of drugs by withholding his allowance (his lunch money was nominal). But he learned soon enough how to get the drug that his body craved. I remember him nearly emptying his savings account of hundreds of dollars the Christmas before his death. I asked him about it and he said he was buying Christmas gifts for friends. But we rarely saw shopping bags while he was supposedly buying gifts. When that money ran out, he became a meth dealer (I cringe at the image my mind conjures up). I never noticed that he had lots of money or things that money could buy, but several of his friends told me at Cameron's memorial service that he always treated at restaurants. Cameron gave me a beautiful photograph of an orchid that last Christmas. He knew I loved orchids and photography so he felt sure I'd appreciate that gift. He was so very right. It hangs in my bedroom today reminding me of the special connection I had with my son.

Dammit, I have to go Christmas shopping tonight. I have $30...that seems enough to finish things up. Go Christmas! The holiday joy is filling my mind with high hopes for an amazingly fresh, new year. Fuck that. Christmas is only four days away, and every second it's pissing me off more and more. Sometimes hate isn't a strong enough word.

3. Liquefied – powdered meth can be liquefied by adding water. Meth can then be injected into a vein or muscle via a needle and syringe.

4. Crystallized – commonly called "ice" or crystal meth is chunks of meth hardened and smoked in a glass pipe with a bulb at one end. If that's not available (or if their pipe breaks as it often does), a light bulb with the end broken off will work as well. In either case, the ice is placed in the bulb, the underside is heated and the smoke that is created is inhaled. (www.drugfree.org/meth360)

As mentioned previously, meth is highly addictive. Users quickly learn the fastest way to get the drug into their bloodstream is via injecting or smoking. The faster meth is absorbed into the body, the more intense the rush. In order to avoid crashing users will binge by taking the drug again and again. This cycle often keeps the users awake for days. Meth users eventually reach a point where no amount of the drug will sustain their high. In this phase, called "tweaking," they may become extremely frustrated, irritable, and likely to be involved in a fight or accident. Users may also self-medicate with a depressant such as alcohol, causing life-threatening health risks.

Environmental Evidence of Meth Use

If meth is snorted, then you may find rolled up paper money, short straws, pieces of glass or mirrors as well as razor blades. If the drug is injected, watch for burned spoons, surgical tubing, syringes, and needles. If meth is smoked, be on the lookout for cans with holes punched out, meth pipes (made of glass), Q-tips with brown or black residue on the cotton tip (used

I noticed in the days leading up to Cameron's death that he was staying out all night without sleep, binging on anything sweet he could find in the house, and was nervous and shaky. He was hanging out with his drug friends skateboarding and buying meth to sell and use. I found out quite a lot about his final days from the journal I discovered in his room after finding him dead. For his last week, the journal was the keeper of Cameron's random thoughts, poetry, hopes for the future, meth escapades, and life conflicts. Yes, he was looking forward to starting college but the meth clouded his thinking and stood in his way of success.

to clean out pipes), and broken light bulbs. Finally, watch for tiny baggies about the size of a half dollar which is the way meth is packaged and sold. I can't begin to tell you how many of these baggies we found in Cameron's room over time. He also had several in his wallet at the time of his death.

Long-term Effects from Persistent Use

Memory loss, hypertension, damage to heart valves, increased risk of strokes, and neurological damage are some of the most profound long-term effects of meth use. The changes that occur within the brain can be equivalent to 40 years of aging and contribute to a greater chance of developing Parkinson's disease in later life. The use of unsterilized needles naturally introduces a myriad of health issues. This may be why users prefer to smoke or snort the drug.

Getting off Meth

If you've found incriminating evidence that your teen may be using meth, do not hesitate to test him. You have the right to test your children and to investigate their rooms. Don't worry about their feelings or that they may not like you or that they think you don't trust them. You don't trust them, you just found evidence!

Go to your local drugstore and buy a drug test for whichever drugs you suspect they might be taking. Some tests require you to mail the test back to the lab for an answer, but others will provide an instant response similar to a pregnancy test. Some schools are pro-active regarding drug use and offer free drug tests to parents if they suspect their child is using

drugs. Ask your school's counselor if they have drug tests available. If the test comes back negative, then you can rest easy. But do not hesitate to test regularly or randomly. Random testing is a good deterrent. If the test comes back positive, now is the time to step in and save your teen's life. Meth addicts must be admitted into an in-patient (lives on the premises day and night) or out-patient (only attends during the day) rehabilitation program depending on the severity of addiction. Rehab lasts from six months to more than a year. The first step in rehabilitation is de-tox.

Addicts typically do not experience a severe physical withdrawal from meth but rather a feeling of anhedonia, which is the inability to experience pleasure. The withdrawal period includes depression, inability to sleep, and increased appetite. They may also exhibit excessive yawning, sneezing, sweating, and have a runny nose and watering eyes. More severe withdrawal symptoms are diarrhea, vomiting, trembling, cramps, confusion, seizures, and possible coma. Users may also become suicidal during this stage. Withdrawal can be alleviated by using meth again.

Unfortunately, many meth addicts who complete rehab return to using after six months. That illustrates how powerful the drug can be.

After de-tox, the most effective rehabilitative interventions include individual and group counseling. Rehabilitated meth users are encouraged to find a new circle of non-drug-using friends. They are also taught stress-coping skills. Narcotics Anonymous or Alcoholic Anonymous groups are very helpful to recovering addicts and are often

(This was Cameron's last entry in the green book. He died later that same morning.)

Thursday morning...

   I swear...karma's kicking my ass. I wrote Lauren a note because it's hard for me to talk about the way I feel about things...so I get to the end, drive to her house, pick a flower from the neighbor's yard, and go up to her car to place her presents inside. As soon as I try to open the locked door, I feel sprinkles. Then it gets harder...then harder...in seconds it's pouring. I let the letter and flower stay sticking out the door, and walked back to my car through the curtain of individual droplets.

   Even through a desperate attempt at saving myself but a fraction of a point, nature foils my plans. It's almost as if I can't catch any relief...but that's bullshit, because ...great. My pipe just broke. I need to pause for reflection now.

recommended by their counselors. They must learn to steer clear of triggers that may cause a yearning to return to meth's grip. There's always a high risk for relapse because the drug damages the executive functions and pleasure-seeking parts of the brain.

CAMERON's suicide attempts

My son never admitted to trying to end his life. However, there were many incidences that I now see as highly suspicious. There was one time Cameron told us that he took a bunch of melatonin. We didn't consider this could be a suicide attempt, so we laughed about it with Cameron because he didn't realize melatonin was a natural substance and we knew no harm could come to him.

In another incident, he took an overdose of pain meds that his girlfriend had given him while on a flight back from NYC with her theater group from school. I went to the airport to pick him up and found him incoherent on the baggage carousel while his girlfriend held him up. Cameron was talking gibberish on the way home from the airport and he asked me to pull over so he could throw up. I didn't know about the pills (he did not tell me until many months later). I assumed he was just tired – he had been in NYC for the past three nights and certainly was up most of the time.

Sometimes it takes more stupidity than
courage to step into the unknown...

SIX

Suicide

Suicide – what an ugly word and image for many, many people. But to the very distressed, it could sound like heaven beckoning to them. It's mind boggling that people can be so tortured that they must end their lives. Many people who take their lives never give any indication that life is this unbearable, even after death (they rarely leave suicide notes like they do in the movies). Frequently after a loved one takes his life, the survivors discover life issues or situations that they believed to be inconsequential, but upon reflection realize were of great importance to the deceased. In hindsight, survivors may also realize that the deceased's drug and alcohol use was related to depression and ultimately led them to suicide.

Attempted Suicide

In the news and in our lives we hear about suicides, but we rarely hear about attempted suicides. The American Association of Suicidology states someone attempts suicide every 40 seconds and on average there are 25 attempts for every completed suicide; three times more women than men attempt suicide but four times more men than women succeed (men use more lethal means, i.e., guns and hanging). In the U.S. in 2006, there were 33,300 suicides. For non-mathematical types like me, that translates to 832,500 attempts! Young people ages 15-24 make up 12.6% of that number (4,189). Several studies completed in 2007 discovered these disturbing facts about students in grades 9-12 (www.teensuicidestatistics.com; AACAP).

When we got home, he went straight to bed but got up a couple times to throw up again. I took Cameron to our family doctor the next day and he did not mention (more like confess) taking the pills. I wish our doctor had assumed something such as a drug overdose, but he shrugged his shoulders and gave Cameron medicine for nausea and sent us on our way. I feel Cameron's dad, who had passed away the year before, was watching over his boy, and protecting him. His dad could get him out of this one but not his final suicide mission.

He also toyed with cutting himself but only ended up with red marks and scars on his arms. When I asked him about the markings, he said it was nothing. I chalked it up to depression - never imagining he would go farther. Cameron participated in the craze of abusing Triple C, slang for Coricidin® Cough and Cold, a common over-the-counter antihistamine medication. In his bedroom, hidden away, we would find many empty foil sheets of Coricidin®. Cameron told me once that he took two sheets of tabs to see what would happen. He would experience some type of high and then sleep for many hours. I think now that surely death must have entered his mind.

In each one of these statistics twice as many females as males were represented. According to the National Conference of State Legislatures (NCSL):

- 19.3% seriously considered suicide
- 14.5% made actual plans for committing suicide.
- 6.9% reported one suicide attempt (2 million)
- 2% reported one suicide attempt requiring medical attention (700,000)

From an Oprah Winfrey transcript to people, especially teenagers, who think that suicide is the answer, AJ begs them to reconsider. "If we just step back and strive towards tomorrow, it will get better," he says. "And the day after that will be better than the day before. So never give up. You don't know how many people you're going to hurt by leaving them behind."

May 2, 2005

Days diminishing, no work to be done.

My life seems pointless

the assholes have won.

I want to die.

No more, no less

to stop this shit

and end this quest.

An empty journey

through dead terrain...

I found my solace

to end my pain.

    take a knife

    against my vein

    press and pull

    to spill the pain.

Why help is not always sought (National Institute for Mental Health)

1. Belief that nothing could help
2. Seeking help is a sign of weakness or failure
3. Reluctance to admit having problems
4. Denial of problems
5. Too embarrassed

In this NIMH study, lack of insurance coverage and not being able to afford treatment were less significant barriers than the barriers related to mental health stigma. Regarding teens, the studies show that they may fail to seek help because they think no one understands them or that they have no one to turn to.

Recovery from a Suicide Attempt

If you are recovering from a suicide attempt (or supporting someone who is), there are steps you can take to get back on the right track and reduce the risk of a future suicide attempt. Remember, everyone's recovery is different and different methods work for different people.

1. **Create a safety plan with your doctor or therapist.** Keep a written copy so you can refer to it when necessary. Know where it is at all times. Don't hide it!

2. **Build a support system.** Choose a close friend or family member – someone to be your ally, someone you can trust and be totally

Awakening to the Sounds of Alley Cats Pimping
the Existence of Life

laughing
everyone's always laughing
what's so fuckin funny?
smirks and grins
must be wonderful for such joyful thoughts
to run through your veins like honey
love and beauty
giving people reasons to live
and they say it's the simple things in life
I have neither witnessed nor owned either of these necessities
but I do know the simplest thing to do with my life
and this can easily be done with a wrist and a knife
everyone at sometime has joked about death
and what a fun thing to joke about
but I myself am not like the rest
some fear death
I laugh at it
for what have I to lose?
I have neither love nor beauty in my life that I am aware of
all I would be is a memory in the veer of someone's mind

(continued)

honest with. You must be able to share any feelings or thoughts of ending your life. You can choose more than one person.

3. **Participate in a mutual peer-support group.** Learning from others and sharing your experiences can make a big difference in your life. And the way you think about your life.

4. **Learn to live again!** Get back into a routine. Eat at regular times, exercise regularly (skateboarding, dancing, anything to get your body moving), and go to sleep and get up at the same time every day. Participate in a fun activity. It might be photography, going to the movies, or collecting special items of interest. Your activity can carry you through a tough moment and bring you comfort and happiness. If the routine is too much for you, refer to your safety plan or ally for help.

5. **Remove the means for hurting yourself from your environment.** No guns, no stock piling pills, no alcohol, no association with toxic people.

6. **Identify and conquer irrational thoughts.** Some people have persistent thoughts of suicide. For others, these thoughts may accompany certain moods or circumstances. Events and visuals such as an anniversary or seeing a knife in the kitchen can cause your thoughts to spiral. Plan to minimize the effects of these triggers. Try to avoid them if possible or train yourself to respond

a distant memory they'd wish to never find
only one true friend I have left
and I fear I'm fading from his mind just like the rest
besides, ending this jest of a life might be for the best

Cameron Stephenson

I look back now and did not consider that Cameron would take his life. I was being proactive. I took him to therapists and they were supposed to be on the lookout for suicidal tendencies–or so I thought. After all, I didn't go to school to learn how to evaluate my child's mental health – most parents don't. I remember standing and looking out our kitchen window, wondering what I would do if Cameron did take his life. This is such a vivid memory. I was not sure of the answer and prayed that it would never come to fruition. Funny how I can see myself standing there, arms crossed, wondering. It must have been a premonition. Damn.

differently. Life events do not cause a suicide, but they can increase the risk of an attempt. Medication can help as can self-help books and affirming messages.

7. **Be evaluated for and learn all you can about mental illness.** Having a diagnosis and information will allow you to have more control and participate in your own self-care.

8. **Know crisis hotline numbers.** Trained people will listen and talk to you, remind you of your safety plan, and point out alternative solutions. Helpful phone numbers are listed in the back of this book.

Completed Suicide

Statistics reveal that many depressed individuals who are unsuccessful at their suicide attempts will keep trying until they are successful. The Centers for Disease Control and Prevention reports a) suicide is the third leading cause of death for teens and young adults preceded by accidents and homicides and b) suicide is the fourth leading cause of death for young people between the ages of 10 and 14. Twelve young people ages 15-24 are lost every day to suicide:

That's one beautiful, brilliant life lost every 2 hours.

I'm 18 years old into it,

and I'm already sick of life.

I've seen enough...

and it makes me heart-broken

to keep living in this mess

of a world. If people are

lame enough to kill over

opposing religious beliefs, what

good am I? I can't change

anything. So why live, trying to?

Quitting was invented for the thoughtful...

there's nothing negative about it.

Methods of Suicide

Suicide is almost always a violent death. The following numbers are for completed suicides amongst U.S. teens and young adults ages 14 to 24, which in 2005 totaled 4,665 (CDC/WISQARS).

Cause of death	Percentage %	Actual Number
Suicide by firearms	46.5	2,269
Suffocation/hanging	37.2	1,812
Poisoning/overdose	8.4	411
Fall	2.5	124
Drowning	.9	42
Cut/pierce	.6	26
Transportation related	.5	28
Fire/burn	.5	17
Unspecified	.3	14

Many suicides, as well as attempts, can be disguised as accidents: car crashes, drug overdoses, binge drinking, the "choking game," getting "stuck" on train tracks, drowning. Only those who left us know their true intentions. Because firearms are the number one choice for completing suicide, especially among males, properly storing firearms and ammunition or removing them altogether from your home is highly

Cameron saw his psychiatrist the week before he took his life. I sure wish his doctor had listened to my concerns about Cameron being more depressed than usual. The doctor feels the same way, too. Yet his doctor explained to me after Cameron's death that some depressed people are determined to end their lives, no matter what we do to try to help them. Sometimes no amount of therapy or antidepressants can keep our teens alive. This psychiatrist told me he will listen to the mothers of his patients more carefully now. He realizes that mothers do know their children best.

Hopeless ambition

neglected intuition

pointless superstition

hidden apparition

recommended, especially if a known depressed individual lives with you or visits your home. Studies have found that the gun used in 82% of firearm suicides by youth under age 18 belonged to a family member.

Causes Associated With Suicide

What causes a teen to take his life? How can life be so miserable (particularly in this great country of freedom, wealth and opportunity) that death appears more appealing than living? These are gnawing, disturbing questions for those who have lost someone to suicide, especially because most of the time "the" reason is never truly known, and likely there were many reasons that even the deceased person wasn't aware of. Still, we always want and feel the need to know WHY? Eventually most survivors of suicide select one or two plausible reasons to ease their minds. The following are typical "reasons" associated with teen suicide.

Mental Disorders

It is believed that more than 90% of completed suicide victims had one or more **mental** disorders (American Association of Suicidology). Disorders that are most likely associated with suicide are: depression (a primary factor), drug and/or alcohol dependency, conduct disorders (in adolescence), schizophrenia, and personal crises. Most of these people were under a doctor's care at the time of their attempted or completed suicide. Approximately 50% of those who die by suicide in America will have seen a mental health provider at some time in their life.

In Chapter 2 I discussed extensively the physiological and situational causes of **Depression.** When you understand the thinking of a depressed

Something Wicked this Way Comes

To have so many things I want to
say, but be at a loss of words.
The thoughts I wish to preach
are thoughts that people have
heard.
On warm summer nights,
especially of late,
I've pondered the thought of
death and whether I want to
wait.
But I think I've become somewhat
timid in the proceedings of my
"crime."
Maybe I'm simply
procrastinating,
waiting for a better time.
"No better time than the
present," people like to say.
Tomorrow's worthless agenda
has proven it to be this way.
So I write with pen and paper

the issues that I've thought.
But nothing seems to cheer me
up: my emotions are distraught.
I wish that all my melancholy
thoughts and true desires,
would be carried away on heavy
wings of a raptor that never
tires.
To saw "farewell forever"
to the treacheries of yore,
and then letting something
blossom; something to adore.
But that's a dream, a fairy-
tale; nothing tangible or true.
So for now I'll sit in sadness,
for there's nothing else to do.
The sun will rise, then later set.
My life is but a jest.
Something kill me soon, I beg of
thee...
to put my presence to rest.

(Author's note: The tears flow and my stomach knots whenever I read this poem as I feel it must have been written shortly before Cameron finally proceeded with ending his life.)

person, you can almost understand how suicide could seem logical to them. Depressed individuals think more slowly, have a hard time concentrating on homework or projects, are easily distracted, and have memory difficulties. They also tend to recall negative experiences more readily than positive ones and in greater detail. They suffer from poor self-esteem to the nth degree. They typically have an all or nothing problem-solving model and many thinking errors (e.g., "Bad things always happen to me."). They feel pain acutely and have difficulty predicting positive outcomes for the future (e.g., "I am always going to be in pain and things are never going to get better.").

In a 2004 national survey of youth aged 14-17, on average per year nearly 900,000 teens had made a plan to kill themselves during a major depressive episode, and 712,000 actually attempted suicide (National Survey on Drug Use and Health).

Conduct Disorder (CD) is a rare condition characterized by a persistent pattern of anti-social behavior that often includes aggression to people and animals, destruction of property, and serious violation of family and societal rules. CD is almost always a result of dysfunctional family life including childhood abuse and neglect. Conduct-disordered teens are vulnerable to suicide because they often lack a moral compass and a sense of belonging to something or someone positive.

Although **Schizophrenia** is rare in teenagers (onset is usually late adolescence or early adulthood) it is still considered a contributing factor to causes of suicide. Schizophrenia is characterized by gross impairment in reality testing and incoherent speech. A schizophrenic is unable to correctly evaluate his perceptions and thoughts or those of other people.

I should mention that our family, my husband, son, and I – were under a great deal of stress at the time of Cameron's death. I had lost my full-time job in March that year, so I was stressed job hunting. We knew Cameron was doing meth but he refused to go back into rehab – he knew his rights as an adult. My husband, Dan, was stressed from his demanding job (he worked from home at the time) and he was frustrated over Cameron's issues. It felt as if we were about to explode.

As much as I hate to admit this, Cameron's death did bring some relief to our house. The stress of what to do about Cameron was gone. Of course, I would trade the grief for the stress right this minute. I would love to have the opportunity to continue helping Cameron kick his addictions and conquer his depression.

Once nothing exists,

everything is a happy memory.

He therefore makes incorrect assumptions, has delusional thinking, and acts inappropriately in most situations. Schizophrenics are vulnerable to suicide because of their thinking disorder and the isolation that it causes.

Other Contributing Factors

➤ Research suggests that teen boys who take their lives were depressed, aggressive, quick-tempered, impulsive, and had relationship difficulties. Fifty percent of these teens were likely to have been involved in binge or heavy drinking and/or drug abuse prior to death (NVISS). The use of **drugs and alcohol** breaks down inhibitions and facilitates impulsive and thrill-seeking behavior. Using drugs and alcohol prior to attempting suicide likely dulls the senses and gives them courage to complete the task at hand – ending their lives. (Cameron had a high level of methamphetamine in his bloodstream when he died).

➤ Another contributing factor to teen suicide is a **crisis event.** Many teens experienced a crisis event in the 24 hours prior to their suicide: the breakup with a girlfriend or boyfriend, trouble with the legal system (a pending court date), a bad grade on a test, public humiliation, being bullied, or an argument gone badly with parents or a relative. These situations may seem trivial to an adult, but can feel larger than life to a teen. A teen who has contemplated suicide is vulnerable to following through as an impulsive reaction to these situations; it's a "combustible fusion when triggered by an adverse or painful event" (Redison, p.90).

Torment is only a gesture
when I sit alone.
finally discover the cure

the final solution is simple
but still there's nothing I can do
no way to get through.

     I just hate you
     but not the things you do
     or that way you chew
     you make me want to
     spew...
     simply 'cause I fuckin'
     hate you!

Forgive and forget, fuck that
How can I forget a plague

I just wish I could attack
you...

Like an incurable disease
you just refuse to cease
you're droning.

Just do what it takes
and make no mistakes
when you tie your noose.

So drop dead;
Fucking anything instead
of driving me mad
Just make me want to
sometimes I need to ...
I fucking hate you.

➢ Family issues can make some teens vulnerable to suicide.

- **Absence of roots** – traditional extended family is unavailable to many children due to our mobile American society. Many families do not stay in the same location long enough to put down roots in their communities. Children who lack a sense of belonging are vulnerable to many risk factors in life.

- **Lack of Parental Time** of Skills – some parents don't have the time and some don't have the capacity to provide their children with an adequate amount of supervision, emotional support, guidance and a sense of belonging. A study by Colleen Alexander-Roberts suggests that almost all teens (99%) believe their parents don't understand them, but as many as two-thirds feel they have inadequate relationships with their families. To satisfy their needs kids will solicit emotional support from their peers; some will become vulnerable to gang participation. Unfortunately, research shows that the amount of time children spend in unsupervised peer interactions is negatively correlated with child outcomes. That is, the more time they hang out with their friends, the poorer they do in life: the blind leading the blind!

Cigarettes staining my fingers
a dull pastel,
I walked away, and now I can tell
she really did care.
The lies I told, more than a few,
Words passed between us are
far overdue,
but I'll drink the poison instead.
Today I actually made a noose.
It lay, asleep in my car, ready
and waiting for me to snap.
Poised and anxious, ropes snap
back twice as hard.
Suicide isn't my new admiration,
but then it never has been.
I aim to live, but happily.
Still, in this world it's hard to
win.

The smoke is burning my eyes
and my tears are tearing me
down.
Windows into my soul don't open,
but that's all she wanted.
Curiosity tempting her to peak
in, to gaze at the unseen.
Unknown, untouched and unkept.
Why I close the blinds to this
barren place, I'm not sure. Even
the most vicious tiger has
stripes to hide him from his
prey. A past-time taken up by
the weak, praying.
I can't eat anything, my
stomach's a knot.
At least knots are
strong...too bad I'm not.

➢ **Parental expectations** that are too high, parents who live vicariously through their children or who need their children to succeed as proof of their own self-worth negatively impact their teen's self-concept, causing identity confusion.

➢ **Loss of hope** over an extended period of time can be devastating to one's state of mind. Some teens lose hope when their future appears unpredictable. For example, in these times of economic uncertainty some teens can't envision how a college education will guarantee a job or future success in life. Some lose hope when they don't even expect to make it into their twenties.

➢ Research from the National Institute on Drug Abuse has shown that **violence on TV**, and in films, video games and music can be hazardous to your health, particularly if you are young and vulnerable. Observing violence in and of itself will not cause a teen to act out violently. However, those teens who have a penchant for violence may be reinforced to act violently by observing or listening to violent media (www.drugabuse.gov).

NEVER IGNORE THREATS OF SUICIDE!

National Suicide Hotline
1-800-SUICIDE (1-800-784-2433)
National Suicide Prevention Lifeline
1-800-273-TALK (1-800-273-8255).

Throughout Cameron's last week he displayed some of the suicidal waning signs. He stopped taking showers but tried to fool me into thinking he was taking them by letting the water run for long periods of time. I was confused by his behavior. Sometimes my sweet Cameron would surface, other times he ignored me. He didn't seem to care about anything anymore. Was it the drugs or the decision to end his life? He was smoking more meth than usual that week. (I found out from his friends later that was the case.)

After his death, I discovered my missing garnet necklace in my jewelry armoire. I was never quite sure what had happened to that necklace, but after its mysterious reappearance I knew that Cameron had taken it during a weekend we were away. He had thrown a party that weekend (unbeknownst to us) and when I put two and two together I figured maybe it had been stolen. But I was wrong. When Cameron decided his final fail-proof method for ending his life – suffocation by hanging – he returned my necklace to its rightful place. I wore the necklace at one of his memorial services. It made me feel a bit closer to him.

Emergency Warning Signs

1. Increased use of alcohol or drugs.
2. Writing or talking about hopelessness and/or revenge ("I don't want to live anymore." or "I'll just kill myself.").
3. Change in sleep, eating or personal hygiene patterns.
4. Increase in agitation – restlessness.
5. Running away from home can be a plea for help.
6. Withdrawal – from friends, family, and society in general. Isolation, no communication with family and friends, spends lots of time in his room.
7. Anger – increase in outbursts.
8. Recklessness – takes part in risky activities, does not care about potential danger or outcome involved.
9. Dramatic mood change.
10. Intense or prolonged grief – perhaps over the death of a loved one.
11. Giving away prized possessions – "tidying up his affairs" Giving away his favorite CDs or skateboard.
12. Suicide ideation – talking (or writing) about hurting or killing themselves, looking for methods to carry out a plan.
13. Threats – **take every threat seriously whether it's written or verbal. Seek professional help immediately if you suspect your teen is in danger**.

I try to train my mind to remember the happy times I had with my son but it's not so easy yet. I surround myself with pictures of when he was young – much happier in those days.

There was one occasion when Cameron and I took a trip to Cedar Island located in the North Carolina Outer Banks when he was six years old. I planned our trip so we'd have to take various ferries to get there. I thought he'd be impressed by the fact that our car was going over the water, but he wasn't. What pleased Cameron was the horseback ride we took the next morning. He was on an older horse and he always remembered the name of that horse yet I don't – "Jerry," maybe. I remember the ride as well because the horses were covered in horse flies and the leader said to just swat them off the horse. I did and got a handful of blood in return for my efforts. Our ride took us out into the ocean surf, which I really enjoyed.

SEVEN

Survival after the Loss

Suicide survivors are family members and friends of a loved one who died by suicide. For the survivors, suicide is different from other types of death because the survivor not only lost a cherished child, friend, relative, or spouse, but they must cope with the knowledge that this person made the decision to untimely end their stay in this world. Those of us left behind are always dumbfounded by our loved one's actions and are never sure what we could have done differently to prevent such a drastic measure. We get angry and self-centered at their actions. We question, "Didn't you think about what this would to do me?" or "How could you leave the kids?" or "How am I suppose to pay the bills?" It's hard to accept that they don't think of us when their pain is so great.

We also can feel guilt and we sometimes torture ourselves with questions and self-condemnation. We question why we didn't see the pain our loved one was experiencing. We think, "I must have been a bad _____ (fill in the blank with mom, father, sister, husband, etc.) not to have stopped you from taking your life." We wonder what could have been done differently while they were in our lives to make them happier. Imagining the final moments before the victim's last breath adds to the torment. In reality, there was probably nothing different we could have done to change

Another memorable Cameron moment was a trip with just the two of us, that time to Toronto, Canada. I was attending a conference and felt because Cameron was 16, he could entertain himself during the time I was attending classes. Before the conference began, we took a trip down to Niagara Falls. Cameron suggested because he had his driver's license, maybe he could drive. I let him and we survived – I also was able to give him highway driving tips, which he later shared with his friends.

We enjoyed exploring Toronto and went on a photo shoot before it got dark. We shot the streets of downtown Toronto – Cameron with his camera and me with my camera. We both tried different techniques and angles of everyday subjects, such as a door.

Photo by
Cameron Stephenson
Dallas Farmers Market 2004

the facts, especially if their depression was well hidden. "An abundance of factors influence a person's course in life. Our lives are endlessly shaped and reshaped by interactions of environment, disposition, personal characteristics, cultural expectations, chance events, and a host of other random factors. No matter how loving or wise or careful we are, we cannot change the unexpected nature of death" (C. Staudacher).

It's difficult enough dealing with our own self-blame but when strangers and friends say the wrong things, it feels like a sword through your heart. I can still remember what people said to me while I was depressed and grieving the loss of my son. I heard things such as "That's the coward's way out" and "so-and-so put the final nails in his coffin." These thoughtless expressions are hurtful and unnecessary. Sometimes we have to help people with the appropriate words because they don't know how we feel or what we're going through. It's okay to tell them that just saying; "I'm sorry" goes a long way.

GRIEVING

Once the shock of the death clears from your mind, you must cope with the agonizing reality of your life without your loved one. You may feel like you are going crazy and wonder if you're mentally ill. You may be suffering from situational depression after the suicide. Most likely, you are grieving.

We both loved to shoot photos. I feel he was much better than me in many aspects. While I was in a conference session, he would go out and photograph people who were sitting on benches, or the homeless sleeping on the ground. He really coveted the freedom the homeless possessed, or perhaps some of the men reminded him of his dad. Cameron kept a couple of these photos on his bedroom mirror. I wish I had asked him what the appeal was with those particular photos. Maybe because that was what he loved – the images he captured with street photography.

I love looking at photos of his handsome face during the last year of his life but then I remember just that – that was the last year of his life. So much pain comes from looking at those last photos.

You know you're grieving when:

> ➢ You feel deep sadness and you understand why you feel sad.
> ➢ You can talk about what happened.
> ➢ The pain is an acknowledgment of the loss.
> ➢ You're angry but you're not destructive (self-injury or breaking things).
> ➢ Your identity remains stable (you're still a mom, wife, sibling, etc.).
> ➢ You say "I wish I would have or could have."
> ➢ You dream of the person.

How long should a survivor expect to grieve? There is no set time; most experts agree that the loss of a loved one can take approximately two years before you feel "normal" again. Eventually, the rollercoaster of emotions will stop at the gate and let you off. Your crying does lessen over time. Hourly turns to weekly, then monthly, and slowly just when you're in remembering mode – holidays, special occasions, anniversaries. But you never forget your loved one.

No doubt, your life is forever changed as the result of a suicide of a loved one and grief is a normal process. Some people turn to medication to help ease the pain but it isn't always necessary. It's okay to grieve and feel the pain of loss. If your grieving has gone too far, though, you may need intensive intervention. Seek out a therapist trained in trauma-focused cognitive behavioral therapy (TF-CBT).

I am an avid believer in attending Survivor of Suicide support groups and have done so since the weeks following my son's suicide. When I passed the recommended two-year anniversary mark (recommended by AFSP as well as other organizations), I became a facilitator myself.

If you are a survivor and have not visited a group of this nature, I strongly encourage you to try one at least once. No one has to tell their story or even speak, but you will find it a great relief to find one place where people understand you and where, if you choose, talk about suicide and not feel the stigma that often comes with it. In group you can talk freely about how you feel about losing your loved one to suicide and others there will understand. Maybe not exactly, but they are hurting as well so they can understand your pain. You will learn that healing does come but it is slow. You will learn that your life is forever changed. Now you have to learn to live in this new world without your loved one.

You know grieving has gone too far when:

- ➢ You feel terror or powerless
- ➢ Your anger becomes destructive or assaultive
- ➢ You can't or won't talk about what happened
- ➢ You think it's your fault
- ➢ You dream of yourself as the victim

Creating a new future without the person you lost will take time. You may find yourself renegotiating your identity. You will find happiness again but you will have to reach inside your heart to remember or find what brought you happiness before the death and seek that out again. Many survivors turn to support groups for help.

Survivors of Suicide (S.O.S.) Support Groups

Survivors struggle with the psychological, emotional, and social repercussions of their loved one's decision the remainder of their lives. Fortunately, the suicide stigma is slowly diminishing as the public recognizes that suicide is associated with mental illness (75% – 90% of the cases) and drug abuse (American Association of Suicidology). Suicide victims die from their disease just as cancer victims die from their disease. One difference is that when we lose someone to heart disease or cancer, we generally have time to prepare ourselves for the eventual death. Not so with a suicide.

It's estimated that each suicide intimately affects at least six other people. This would translate to 4.5 million survivors left by 754,570 suicides from 1980 through 2004 (American Association of Suicidology). Providing

I went to Hospice grief recovery sessions as well as attending Touched by Suicide peer support group meetings (these are for those who have lost someone to suicide). I saw my therapist when I felt the need as well. On August 22nd – 11 days after Cameron died – I started journaling. I did this almost daily the first year after losing Cameron. Every morning when I woke up at 6:15 or so, I would take out my yellow notebook and write a page or two, or even three sometimes, about the issues going around in my head. Just getting some of the why-it-happened on paper seemed to clear my head so I could go out among the living and pretend I was one of them. I didn't feel very alive for most of that year. I would write letters to Cameron as my only means of communication with him. I would write about what I accomplished the day before. Just going to the grocery store alone was an accomplishment to be proud of.

support to someone who has lost a loved one to suicide is a relatively new concept and there is still much study to be done on survivors and how to help them heal. The American Foundation for Suicide Prevention (AFSP) began the year my son was born, 1987.

There are many nonprofit suicide postvention groups now. Suicide survivor groups are a godsend because suicide survivors offer one another understanding and support that cannot be gained elsewhere. They receive and give acceptance and compassion making the resolving phase of grief much less lonely and painful. This can diminish the self-blame, self-punishment, and chaos survivors often experience.

Survivors also tend to join suicide prevention activities. They join organizations to discuss ways to save others, write books, lobby for change, contribute time or money to suicide groups, and speak at local schools or organizations about the tragedy of suicide.

One entry from Carolyn's journal dated Monday 10/3 (05) –

"Went to sleep last night without the TV – Dan wasn't snoring. Wake up at 5:45 am though. Had to pee I guess and then I couldn't go back to sleep – thoughts of Cameron hanging. Got up, looked for his artwork to take to my appointment with Kay (my therapist) and got physically sick – to bathroom to poop. I suppose one day I won't have to poop when reading his (Cameron's) words. He was just so damned depressed and I guess it bothers me that I didn't know the depth of his depression. He had let himself inside that vortex (depression) the last week. I swear I think it was a combination of the girls harassing him and large doses of meth…"

There are S.O.S. support groups in every state and many countries. They may have different names (Touched by Suicide, Those Left Behind), but they are all attended by survivors.

To find a location close to you, visit one of these websites:

www.suicidology.org
(listed under Suicide Loss Survivors)

www.afsp.org
(listed under *Surviving Suicide Loss*)

EIGHT

Help and Advice

Depression Prevention

All teens feel down sometimes. When teens feel down, there are many ways they can cope with these feelings. Focusing on friendships and activities can help develop a sense of acceptance and belonging that can prevent a spiral into depression.

- **Friendships** – Healthy relationships with peers are central to a teen's self-esteem and provide an important social outlet.
- **Activities** – (sports, job, school activities or hobbies) Staying busy helps teens focus on their strengths rather than negative feelings or behaviors.
- **Organizations** – Special programs geared to the needs of adolescents help develop additional interests. Maybe there are some at their school or church. Ask if your teen won't!
- **Adult relationships** – Teens are sometimes afraid to ask for help. Encourage them to talk to a favorite teacher, a friend's parents, or a trusted family friend or relative. As long as they are talking, they can get help.

(Bio from Blogpod, age 18, 2005)

Wouldn't this be considered an "auto-bio"? Uhhh...born in Raleigh, NC, still recovering from twisted childhood, I'm a photographer, a smartass, I'm opinionated, modest, politically radical while still realistic, I like to push emotions out of people (mostly emotions they don't express on a day to day basis), I pay too much attention to detail, I despise the hand that wrote the "bible" and hope to shed obvious light onto a majority of society one day, I'm outspoken, I'm either brutally honest or I tend to leave out certain truths, I am ...very bored with writing all this right now, am currently working on a photographic/graphic portfolio for college, I somehow got stuck in this hell-hole of a state (Texas), I plan on moving to a large city where human emotions are seeping from every corner and where all high, middle and low classes learn to tolerate each others' presence despite certain advantages, apparently I like making huge, run-on sentences about my life, and I'm about to enjoy putting an end to this bullshits. Now, breathe.

If you suspect depression, help can be found at:

- Offices of family physicians, internists, and pediatricians

- Public community mental health centers

- Private psychiatric offices and clinics

- Therapists or other mental health professionals

- University or medical school-affiliated programs

- Local hospital – ask for psychiatry department

- Health maintenance organizations (HMOs)

A call to your medical insurance provider can also direct you to the help you need.

Help For Teens Suffering From Depression

Prescription medication can help those who suffer from depression. Yet if someone is severely depressed, it may take several courses and/or combinations of medications to relieve their symptoms. Do not become frustrated if there is no immediate relief. There are about a dozen different products currently on the market to treat Depression and almost all of them contain an SSRI (Selective Serotonin Reuptake Inhibitor). Some products you may be familiar with are Prozac, Zoloft, Concerta, and Cymbalta.

Your doctor may also prescribe anti-convulsive medications or anti-psychotic medications because they have the pleasant side effect of

I decided to participate in Skills USA because photography is what I plan to do for the rest of my life. I discovered that the only way for me to get what I want is to show how much I care. I am entering Skills USA so that I can show what I can do.

This is definitely the most amazing class I've ever taken. I have never had the perfect opportunity to be able to use both creativity and personality together in school. All during these years of high school, I have been looking for a class that would give me the opportunity to be mature enough to say what I wanted, show what I wanted, and express the emotions I had. This class taught me so many things. As far as photography goes, I haven't learned a whole lot. But this is not a specific class. Everything is used in here (e.g. art, photography, graphics, music, language). So, as far as learning goes, there is not a word that has been spoken in this classroom that I didn't hear. And not a syllable has been forgotten (over-exaggeration). As far as giving students the ability to get a real look into an ad design future, this class covers everything beautifully.

(continued)

lifting the fog of depression. This is considered an "off-label" use of these medications, but it is not an unusual practice.

Thirty percent of people who try prescription medication don't respond well and often need other interventions to relieve their symptoms. Some find vitamin supplements to be helpful. Most people find a combination of medication and therapy work well for them. And 70 - 80% of teens are helped by the combined treatment of antidepressants and talk therapy (The Treatment of Adolescents with Depression study).

Of course types of therapy vary as much as types of medications. A few of the more popular types are: Psychotherapy, which focuses on teaching coping skills, and exploring past events and feelings that are still painful or troubling. Cognitive-Behavioral

Therapy, which focuses on turning negative thinking around to a more positive light, exploring alternative solutions to problems, developing social skills, and setting goals for returning to previously enjoyed activities. Interpersonal therapy focuses on developing healthier relationships at home and school. And family therapy focuses on the dynamics of home life including communication and the mutual need for satisfaction of each member of the family.

Therapy sessions are typically once a week and last 50 minutes. The number of sessions vary upon the individual but it's not unusual for therapy to last a year or longer. If you have depression in your family background, be sure to share this with the therapist. They have no way of knowing this unless you share it.

On top of just the graphic ability, it taught me how to use what I could already do (photography and ranting) to my full extent. I really don't have whole lot more to say. This has just been the most amazing 18 weeks of my high school "career", and I'm thankful for all the patience people have given me for some of the things I've said, done, or even thought. Well, now I'm going to print this. Habe bonum diem.

Just as there are different types of medication to try and different types of therapy, so too are there different types of therapists. Some therapists specialize in adolescents, some in adults and some in family. It's important to find a good fit both in philosophy and method. Choosing a male or female, old or young therapist may matter to your teen. Finding a therapist that you like or that makes you feel comfortable may be less valuable, however, than finding one who challenges you or especially your teen. It's not important whether your teen likes their therapist, but rather that they are getting well.

Therapists usually ask that parents stay involved in their children's treatment. They may ask you to join a session or two and to make sure your teen is taking his meds; stopping an antidepressant suddenly can be deadly. If your child doesn't like the way the medication makes him feel, discuss this with his doctor or therapist so a change can be made.

Those suffering from depression should never abruptly stop taking their medication. Studies have found that doing so can increase the risk for suicide. Instead, contact your doctor and discuss your concerns.

In addition to medication, the right therapy, and the right therapist, many people find added relief when they include physical and social activities in their daily routines.

- Encourage physical activity. Push your teen outside to get some exercise! Exercise is very helpful in relieving the symptoms of depression. Perhaps ask her to go to the gym with you, take a run, walk the dog or go for a bike ride. Suggest him getting involved in school sports.

- Encourage normal sleep patterns. Teens need around nine hours of sleep – in one period, not collectively! Create a peaceful environment: dark, quiet, (no cell phones – take their phone away), no TV in the room, and no Internet. Discourage afternoon naps!

- Encourage social activity – the good kind. Isolation makes depression worse. Help set up friend "dates" for your teen. Offer to take him to some type of special interest class, museum, or sports games.

Living with a Depressed Teen

If your teen has been diagnosed with depression, it can affect your whole family. Studies have shown that when depressed and non-depressed people live together, the non-depressed person is brought down but the depressed person is not brought up. Family members of a depressed

"Infinite Commitment"

> Situations slowly growing more pathetic.
> I'm missing something again. Her.
> It's time to mature and let go...completely.
> Decide how and when is a problem
> that constantly raises its brow and smirks.
> It's easy to say the word "forever."
> I hate it. It's another conundrum.
> Nothing is infinite...yet forever seems to exist.
> And quite painfully as well.

I've come to determine that I have
a need to constantly want something.
Call it chaos, perhaps.
When everything is in solace, I start getting bored
With boredom comes chaos...curiosity, enlightenment,
destruction, resentment.
It's almost like a cycle...monocycle and unicycle.

(Continued)

teen will feel exhaustion, rejection, despair, aggravation and other negative emotions. Here are some helpful strategies.

- Remember that your teen is suffering from a real brain dysfunction; he's not behaving this way on purpose.
- Be supportive and try not to get frustrated with them. Getting upset with a depressed teen only isolates them further and can discourage and impede progress.
- Be available to talk no matter how frustrated you may get with your teen. If a teen feels he can talk to you about anything anytime, then you have a greater chance of avoiding disaster.
- Listen without lecturing. Resist the urge to criticize or pass judgment once your teenager begins to talk. The important thing is that your child is communicating.
- Validate their feelings. Don't try to talk teens out of their depression, even if their feelings or concerns seem silly or irrational to you. Simply acknowledge the pain and sadness they are feeling. If you don't, they will feel like you don't take their emotions seriously.
- Avoid offering unsolicited advice or ultimatums
- Be alert to changes in your teen. Ask yourself "Is this (behavior or mood) typical of my child?" If not, what has changed in his life?
- Have hope
- Learn all you can about the condition
- Talk regularly to all family members (no family secrets!)
- Minimize stress at home

Like the current chaotic thought in my mind.
I'm not with Lauren. I'm with Kelly.
Commitment? I miss Lauren's touch...her
soft words. I know she's had a few one-night
stands in her life...this is why I wanted to
be different for her. I wanted to give her my
love as opposed to my lust. But I fucked up.
Commitment...a means to an end. It ties into the
previous discussion of "forever" and the non-existent
infinity. To an extent, it's great...then not.
I don't wish to be "committed" to Lauren, but
I want to be the one she thinks about
while ignoring someone else's conversation.
I want to share every inch of my personal
space with her...to feel her as she breathes.
And I want her to want me. For some
reason, I want reassurance that in two months,
she won't' be pressing those lips against another's.
I feel that's asking too much, but I can't avoid
the paranoia. She probably won't take me
back, anyways. After all, I'm just another boy.

- Change your expectations
- Reach out and get support – from your friends, a support group or your own therapist

Suicide Prevention

Talk openly to them – do not shy away from mentioning suicide. If they are thinking about it, then they might be able to talk about it. Do not tell them, "You have your whole life ahead of you" – they don't care. Instead, gently and calmly question them about how long they've felt this way and if they understand why they feel this way. Ask if they know how they'd end their life and if they have a plan. This open communication should be a relief for your teen.

Suicidal teens want to live but they also want the pain they are feeling to go away. A detailed plan is obviously very serious so call your family physician, psychologist or therapist, a suicide prevention center, or take them to the emergency room. If there is no clear suicide plan and you don't feel he's in immediate danger, still seek professional help <u>as soon as possible</u>. You may be able to save your teen with just one call.

Dispelling time

in uneasy waves,

we drone on living

until our graves.

Seemingly pointless,

we live our life.

Joining in wedlock,

the groom & his wife.

To further branch off

of your family tree,

with love so blinding

that you never see.

Maturing in age

for the common good,

your purpose in life

was misunderstood.

Not to live & steal

you were always

taught,

but learned winning a

battle

is in how it's fought.

Corrupted through media's

sick influence,

you've lost your grasp

on common sense.

Now you believe all

the lies you're told;

your hopes of trust,

practically sold.

So why even write,

trying to inform?

Chances of change

are ripped & torn.

I'll stop this now

and let you be

to live your lies

in misery.

Substance Abuse Prevention

1. Early diagnosis and treatment of learning disorders, attention-deficit-hyperactivity disorder, and mood disorders may reduce the risks of substance use and other associated behavioral and mental health problems. You don't want your teen to start self-medicating as some will if they have a hard time concentrating in class.

2. Be an involved parent. Get involved at their school, meet the teachers and communicate with them on a regular basis – not just at "meet the teacher" nights. Get to know your teen's friends <u>and</u> their parents. All these alliances can help alert you to what's going on in your teen's world. The National Institute on Drug Abuse (NIDA) shows that appropriate parental monitoring protects against the risks of problem behaviors including substance abuse.

3. Open and honest communication. This may seem one-sided most of the time but you must continue to create an open environment for conversation with your teen. Include in your conversations family rules and attitudes about drug and alcohol use. Meal times together at a dining table are a great time for this.

4. Make a pact with them that says they can call you at anytime – day or night – if they need a ride away from a bad situation. No questions asked – at least not at first.

5. Give them permission to make you the bad guy by telling their friends, "My dad will kill me if I do that" or "You know how crazy my mother is!" This allows the teen an excuse to say NO and still save face.

Now that passion is found over—
rated
my love stays delegated
highest bidder
Walk the alleys
just adding to tallies
on love's dirty calendar.
Precious nights
those loving fights
only left me bruises.
Touching fingers
only linger
when the moment's everlasting.
Wreaking of lust
salary tucked, must
be just enough for the tax:

Scraped knees, bruised thighs
a harlot's punishment through
teary eyes.
Soft silence before the storm
her body no longer smooth and
warm
but rancid hair, freshly worn
stale.
Home is no cozy, crisp bed
tending her wounds, preparing
for the night ahead
Sleep is only a dream, dreams
vanquished.
That barrel's sweet taste,
matches life's lonely waste
as she pulls the trigger.

Help for Substance-Abusing Teens

Living with an addicted teen can be a terrible hardship for the entire family. Heated arguments, lying, stealing from others – all account for rocky family relationships. You should not be expected to live under the reign of a teen addict! But here's the dilemma…

You know all the obvious signs and you had the talk with your teen, but he persists in getting "trashed" anyway and you find drugs in his room. What do you do? I posed this question to myself, and my friends with the same problems posed the question to me. I am asked this question so often that it's frightening. Websites are mostly no help. They merely suggest talking to your teen; they don't address what to do when you've found the drugs.

Intervene by getting your teen into a rehabilitation facility. The sooner the better. Early evaluation and treatment can reduce the risks of becoming fully addicted. There are several individual and family-based treatment approaches that are effective in treating substance use in both adolescents and adults. Look in your phone book under mental health facilities or for a drug abuse facility in your area. Call your family physician or insurance company. Do not stress over the "right thing to do" – just act on your impulse so you can save your teen and your family.

Note that teens with substance use disorders have a higher risk of having co-occurring mental health problems, such as depression or ADHD, compared to non-substance-involved teens. Do not expect to resolve both issues with just an anti-depressant. It often takes a variety of medications to correct the different problems.

To her I give my honest love
and want to keep her dearly,
but she's so fragile, as if a
dove,
and I see no motives clearly.
She hides emotion from sound
and sight
but tells me she loves me so.
And she thinks of me on lonely
nights
and it helps our love to grow,
or so it's said and I believe
our love is slipping through a
sieve.
I don't even know what or why,
but her inspiration makes me
cry
alone some nights wishing I was
dead
without worrying about the
future instead.
To die today is no longer a
threat...
but more like a 10-1 against my
bet.

I hope for nothing, that pointless
sleep.
Yet sometimes I want, my life
to keep.
My mood drifts, but she tried
to please,
when all I want is to be
appeased.
And she knows it's hard and
she helps me some,
but there's nothing she does to
keep me from a gun.
I want to leave and simply be a
memory.
a flake of the crust of history.
Screw age and marriage, it's
nothing great.
I doubt I'll make it to twenty-
eight.
Perhaps before I die, maybe in
ten,
I'll finally get to be with Erin.
Blah, blah, blah...stop bitching,
Cameron...
You know you love them all.
Even the ones you don't have.

House Rules for Struggling Teens

Parents need to be firm and flexible, and allow teens to make choices and to suffer the consequences or reap the benefits of their choices. However, when raising a high-risk teen, it's counterproductive to allow flexibility when the teen often makes poor choices and consequences can be life threatening. Most therapists and parenting experts agree that having clear house rules can prevent conflict and help your teen feel secure. Here are some suggestions for House Rules.

Non-negotiable Rules

1. No skipping classes or whole days of school
2. No sneaking out of the house
3. No selling or using drugs or alcohol
4. No physical violence towards others
5. No self-mutilation or suicidal attempts
6. No harm or threat of harm to others
7. No smoking in the house

Negotiable Rules

1. Music off during sleeping hours
2. To bed by 11:00 p.m. Sunday – Thursday
3. When leaving the house, we must know the following:
   - People you'll be with
   - Location
   - Verifiable information
   - When we call your mobile you must answer or call back within the hour
4. Homework to be done nightly (and completely!)

5. Curfew on school nights/other nights: 10:00 p.m.

6. Curfew on weekends: 11:00 p.m.

7. In order to spend the night at a friend's house, I need:
    - Name
    - Address/phone number at house
    - Verification from parent

8. Chores:
    - Empty dishwasher when clean
    - Remove trash from upstairs on Monday nights
    - Dirty clothes downstairs by 8:00 a.m. Sundays
    - Bathroom to be cleaned on (specific day and time)
    - Your room is to be kept tidy (vacuumed, dusted, picked-up; specific day and time)

Above and Beyond Contributions (can be rewarded with money)

1. Cook dinner for family

2. Wash car with soap, sponge, water and then dry with cloth

3. Mow grass

4. Edge grass: sidewalk, around house and fences

Agreed upon by:

_____

Parent name   Signature   Date

_____

Child name   Signature   Date

Carolyn and Cameron (age 5) at the beach.

Autobiography written for Senior English class...

"Almost time to start. Drop the black throw. Are the lights ready? Cue the spotlights! The microphone is working, right? Okay, all ready. Raise the reds...and cue Cameron."

That was my introduction. I felt that there was no need for a drum roll, so I thought I might as well just move on. Well, if you, whoever is reading this, are still curious about who this odd little boy is, wait no longer. It is me, Cameron Stephenson, and I'm here, as always, to be engulfed by the wonder and bliss that is, of course, English.

I am seventeen, from Raleigh, North Carolina, am desperately and hopelessly in love with photography, am a Gemini, and enjoy long, brisk walks on the beach when there's a full moon. I have had a pretty unique life so far and intend to keep it that way as long as I live.

Sorry for the lack of detail, but I'm not one to talk about myself. I prefer to let people learn about me as they have more experiences with me. I have come to the conclusion that experiences are a better way to learn than by personal curriculum. So, really I'm very sorry that this is shorter than asked, but sometimes it is more reliable to trust one's eye than it is the written word.

Thank you, and goodnight. "Drop the reds! Cue soft, cheesy music."

Champagne wishes and caviar dreams...

Cameron Stephenson

– FIN –

Biography for Carolyn Zahnow

Carolyn Zahnow is the founder of "Save the teens," a grassroots effort to teach parents, teachers, and mentors of teens the signs of teen depression and substance abuse. She shares her experience of life with her son, Cameron, as he battled the same issues but, unfortunately, lost the battle. Cameron ended his life on August 11, 2005. Along with her suicide prevention efforts, Zahnow also started a local support group for others who have lost a loved one to suicide. The support group holds a community walk in the fall, organized by Zahnow, in an effort to erase the stigma attached to mental illness and suicide.

Zahnow holds degrees in Communication and Marketing Management from North Carolina State University and San Diego City College. She writes articles for various publications sharing her experiences with loss and recovery, and has also been profiled in newspapers in North Carolina and upcoming books by other authors.

She lives in North Carolina with her husband and their dog, Sheila. Cameron was her only child.

Listing of Associations

For more information and help on topics of teen depression, suicide, and all other topics included in this book, visit or call these organizations:

American Association of Suicidology – www.suicidology.org

1-202-237-2280

American College of Emergency Physicians www.acep.org

1-800-798-1822

American Foundation for Suicide Prevention (AFSP) www.afsp.org

1-888-333-AFSP

American Psychiatric Association www.psych.org

1-888-35-PSYCH or 1-888-35-77924

American Psychological Association www.apa.org

1-800-374-2721

Befrienders International/Samaritans www.befrienders.org

Covenant House Nineline Hotline www.covenanthouse.org

1-800-999-9999

Hispanic Community Resource Helpline

1-800-473-3003

Jason's Foundation, Inc. www.jasonfoundation.com

Link's National Resource Center for Suicide Prevention and Aftercare

(LINK-NRC) www.thelink.org

1-404-256-9797

National Alliance on Mental Illness (NAMI) www.nami.org

1-800-950-NAMI (6264)

National Institute of Mental Health (NIMH) www.nimh.nih.gov

1-866-615-6464

National Mental Health Association www.nmha.org

1-800-969-NMHA (6642)

National Mental Health Information Center (NMHIC)

www.mentalhealth.samhsa.gov

1-800-789-2647

National Organization for People of Color Against Suicide www.nopcas.com

202-549-6039

Suicide Awareness Voices of Education (SAVE) www.save.org

1-952-946-7998

Suicide Prevention Action Network (SPAN) USA www.spanusa.org

1-202-449-3600

Suicide Prevention Resource Center www.sprc.org

1-877-GET-SPRC (438-7772)

Survivors of Suicide – to locate a group near you, visit www.afsp.org

National Suicide Prevention Lifeline

1-800-273-TALK (8255)

www.depressedteens.com (Child and Adolescent Bipolar Foundation)

1-847-492-8519

www.kidshealth.org

www.suicide.org/suicide-statistics.html

www.drugfree.org/meth (for further information on meth)

Bibliography and Other Sources

<u>Books</u>

Alexander-Roberts, Colleen. <u>ADHD and Teens: A Parent's guide to making it through the tough years</u>. Dallas: Taylor Publishing, 1995: 150-153, 171.

Bigelow, Barbara C. <u>UXL Encyclopedia of Drugs and Addictive Substances</u>. Vol. 4. Detroit: Thomson Gale, 2006.

Cotter, Bruce. <u>When They Won't Quit: A Call to Action for Families, Friends and Employers of Alcohol and Drug-Addicted People.</u> Hunt Valley, Maryland: Holly Hill Publishing, 2002.

"Emotional and Mental Health." <u>The Gale Encyclopedia of Genetic Disorders</u>. Vol. 1. 2002.

Espejo, Roman, ed. <u>Suicide (Opposing Viewpoints).</u> San Diego: Libri, 2003.

"Mental Health." <u>Grolier Wellness Encyclopedia</u>. Pgs., 74, 91, 98, 100, 111-114, s.v.

Oster, Gerald D. and Sarah S. Montgomery. <u>Helping Your Depressed Teenager: A Guide for Parents and Caregivers</u>. New York: John Wiley and Sons, 1994.

MacMillan Health Encyclopedia, Vol. 5, Gale Group, 1999.

Publications (magazines, brochures, newspapers)

Anderson, S. J. "The Dark Void of Depression," *USA Today*,
> November, 1988: 70-72.

Blakeslee, Sandra. "This is your brain on meth: A forest fire of damage," *The
> New York Times*, July 20, 2004.

Bower, Bruce. "Lifting the Mood," *Science News*, Vol. 166 Issue 8,
> August 21, 2004: 116-117.

Brady, Jonann. "Portrait of a Young Meth Addict," *ABC News*,
> November 2, 2005.

Butterfield, Fox. "States May Restrict Cold Pills with Ingredient in Meth," *The
> New York Times*, January 30, 2005.

Davis, Patti. "Dope: A Love Story," *Time Archive 1923 to the Present*,
> 2005.

Gellman, Rabbi Marc. God Squad, Tribune Media Services, Inc.,
> January 12, 2007.

Jones, Steven and Brittany Stidham. Marcus High School *Marquee*,
> May 2, 2005, 12-13.

Leinwand, Donna. "Meth cases put strain on ERs," *USA Today*,
> January 18, 2006.

Leshner, Alan I. "Methamphetamine," NIDA Community Drug Alert Bulletin,
> 1999.

Moskos, Michelle. "Hope for Tomorrow: Mental Health and Substance
Abuse Education Evaluation in Utah—Part II," Outreach Partnership
Program 2005 Annual meeting, *National Institute of Mental Health*,
> April 3, 2005.

Murphy, Kathryn. "What Can You Do to Prevent Teen Suicide?," *Nursing
> 2005*, December, 2005, Vol. 35, Number 12:43–45.

Papakostas, George I. "The Newest Brain booster" *Alternative Medicine*,
        April, 2005: 59.

Rollert, Diane. "Crying Wolf about Meth Abuse?," *The New York Times*,
        August 11, 2005.

Roosevelt, Margot. "The Cold-Pill Crackdown," *Time Inc.*,
        February 7, 2005.

Steele, Bruce C. "There and Back Again," *Advocate*, Issue 947: 8,
        September 27, 2005.

Volkow, Nora D. "Exploring the Why's of Adolescent Drug Abuse," *NIDA*,
        Vol.19, No.3, September 2004.

Wichern, Dennis. "The War on Meth," *Newsweek*,
        July 30, 2005.

Williams, Armstrong. "Teen Suicide," *New Amsterdam News*, Vol.97 Issue
        2, January 5, 2006:13.

Wysong, Pippa. "Dark Moods," *Current Health,* Vol. 32, Issue 4,
        December 2005: 14-17.

Harvard Injury Control Research Center's NVISS Project

National Institute on Drug Abuse (NIDA)

SAFE-T brochure, National Suicide Prevention Lifeline, Education
        Development Center, Inc. and Screening for Mental Health, Inc.,
        2007.

"Depression – What you Need to Know About Adolescent Depression –
        Helping Depressed Teens," National Mental Health Association
        (2006).

"Methamphetamine Abuse and Addiction," National Institute on Drug Abuse
        Research Report Series, 1998.

"Studies Say Emergency Meth Cases Putting Hospitals in a Fix," *The New
        York Times, reported in Dallas Morning News,* January 18, 2006.

Other Resources (e-news, DVD and interviews)

Jefferson, David J. "America's Most Dangerous Drug," *Newsweek*, URL:
    http://www.newsweek.com/id/56372 (August 8, 2005).

Jordan, Katie, "Depressed Teens Can Get Help." *The Tattoo,*
    December 8, 2003

URL: http://home.comcast.net/~majerus-collins/helpfordepressed.htm.

Kirn/Billings, Walter and Dawson, Patrick. "Crank," *Time*,
    June 22, 1998.

URL: http://www.time.com/time/magazine/article/0,9171,988577-5,00.html

Palsha, Rebecca, "Recovering Meth User Shares Story," MSNBC.com,
    2005.

Schabner, Dean. "Meth Use by Women on the Rise," *ABC News*,
    Oct 25, 2004.

Staudacher, Carol. "Surviving a Violent Death" BeliefNet, *Resources: The
    Journey Through Sorrow*. http://www.beliefnet.com, May 23, 2000.

Segal, Jeanne. "Teen Depression: A Guide for Parents and Teachers,"

Helpguide.org. http://www.helpguide.org/mental/depression_teen.htm

Jessica Jarrard, (LCSW with Seay Behavioral Health Center, Presbyterian
    Hospital of Plano, TX, interview with author, January 2006.

HBO: Addiction, DVD. HBO, 2007.

www.drugabuse.gov/infofax/methamphetamine.html

Index